W9-AZU-812

WYATT EARP'S 13 DEAD MEN

by

Ben T. Traywick

Published by
RED MARIE'S BOOKSTORE
P.O. Box 891
Tombstone, Arizona

Wyatt Earp's Thirteen Dead Men

by
Ben T. Traywick
Published by Red Marie's Books
Tombstone, Arizona
Copyright 1998 by Ben T. Traywick
Front and back cover art by Jill Tong

Author's note:

Before one of the "wannabes" gets excited and
overcome by his own verbosity the author
does not say that Wyatt Earp
killed these 13 men.

CONTENTS

AUTHOR'S INTRODUCTION

The author has long visualized such a book as this one, but had many doubts about creating it. Many friends, readers, and historians have suggested that I should do this. However, such an endeavor needs an explanation to the reader.

First, as in all my writing, I have avoided all social and political correctness, as well as liberals and revisionist historians, all of which had not a damn thing to do with the settling of the West. All of them came along after everything was nice and safe.

What this book will contain is an account of the Earp years in Tombstone taken from the history that I have accumulated during the past thirty years. As every reader of Earpiana well knows there are some blank spots in this history that have not yet been documented. I intend to fill these blanks with what I believe happened from my years of experience in research and writing about the subject. I will also include a number of details that will explain some incidents.

Up to this point all my books have been heavily documented, historical accounts. As I have never written such a book before, I wish my readers to know that this volume can not be called a pure history account. It will not be documented as all my other books are, but will be historically correct except in the areas where I draw the conclusions that are logical and evident to me. Call this book what you will - a novel- a tale of the old west or whatever - it will still tell more of a real story than most of the books written about Tombstone.

I wish my readers to enjoy my efforts in this new adventure and those of you who know me surely realize:

If I didn't believe it, I wouldn't write it!

Ben T. Traywick

PROLOGUE

Tombstone erupted into a boom town when all of Arizona was Apache land. Geronimo, Victorio, and Nachez led their fierce warriors in bloody raids the length and width of southern Arizona. Few white men penetrated this barren, merciless land and returned to tell of it.

In 1877, Edward Lawrence Schieffelin, a determined prospector, riding in company with a band of Hualapai scouts on their way to Fort Huachuca, arrived in the San Pedro Valley. He made the old Brunckow cabin his base of operations. Schieffelin was a tall, wild figure with a full beard and long hair. Although he appeared to be fifty years of age, he had not yet reached thirty.

The tough desert men and soldiers who stopped at Brunckow's accepted him without question because they knew he was a close-mouthed prospector. Schieffelin looked upon the cabin as a haven of rest, safety, and comfort, secure from the Apache.

Ed strictly minded his own business and at first light, he was up and gone into the endless wasteland that led to what is now known as the Tombstone Hills. At dusk, he reappeared, ate his meager supper, then got into his bedroll to await another day.

Through all the daylight hours he searched the dry washes and outcroppings for evidence of ore. On several occasions, he had sighted bands of Apaches near him and had carefully dropped from sight until they had moved on .

The miners and soldiers who had stopped at Brunckow's saw him ride out alone each day and watched for his return at night. Other men had come there, and ridden out alone just as Schieffelin did. The other men had not returned. Soldiers had found what was left of them after the Apaches had ridden on.

At last, one of the young cavalry men (private) at the cabin asked him, "Why do you go off into them hills?"

Edward Lawrence Schieffelin

Born in Tioga County, Pennsylvania in October, 1847, Ed discovered the silver lodes that started the boom town that became Tombstone. He died in Douglas County, Oregon on May 12, 1897. Ed found his Tombstone and he will sleep in the shadow of it for all eternity.

(The Brunckow mine and cabin lies southeast of Tombstone about 9 miles and east of the San Pedro River about 2 miles. It was claimed by Frederick Brunckow, a German mining engineer employed by the New York Mining Company. He built a cabin, a tiny general store, and opened a mine site. His Mexican employees murdered him in 1860 and threw his body down the mine shaft.)

(This cabin has seen more violence than any other spot in Arizona and still holds many dark and bloody secrets yet unknown. There is little left of it now thanks to "shooters", but it is the OLDEST ANGLO STRUCTURE IN ARIZONA.)

"Looking at rocks," Schieffelin replied.

"You keep fooling around out there amongst them Apaches and the onliest rock you'll find will be your tombstone!" blurted the young soldier.

One evening it was too near dark for Ed to return to the cabin. He chose a round topped hill further up the wash for his camp and settled in for the night among some big rocks. After a nervous, restless night, Ed was up at daybreak and headed for the hills. All along the wash he found scattered pieces of silver float.

Moving up the wash he saw a large red and black ledge of silver ore. Ignoring the cactus spines and sharp rocks, Ed climbed up to the ledge. He estimated it to be fifty feet long and twelve inches wide. Ed sunk his pick into the ore and pried out several pieces. They were dark and heavy! Almost pure silver! A strike for sure! He had finally found it. The vein of silver that he had exposed was soft and pure, and a coin pressed into it left a clear imprint.

As he remembered the words "all you'll find out there will be your tombstone," Ed smiled. If the Apaches had found him he probably wouldn't have needed a tombstone. Still, recalling the warning, he mused over the word tombstone. Yet, he liked it! Might make a good name for his claim. He named it the Tombstone and the second one he found the Graveyard.

Although Ed did not realize it at that time he had named not only a mine, but the hills where it lay, an entire silver lode, and a town yet unborn. It would be a town whose fame and riches would astound the world forever.

Ed walked all the way to Signal, where his brother Al worked. It took him awhile to convince Al and Dick Gird, the company assayer, to quit good jobs and go into the mining business with him.

Arriving back in the San Pedro Valley, they set up permanent camp at Brunckow's cabin, where several fresh graves were mute testimony to recent Apache raids.

Ed Schieffelin's last wishes were, "It is my wish, if convenient, to be buried in the dress of a prospector, my old pick and canteen with me, on top of the granite hills about three miles westerly from the City of Tombstone, Arizona, and that a monument, such as prospectors build when locating a mining claim, be built over my graveyard or cemetery." Ed's body was exhumed in Oregon and brought to Tombstone. He was laid to final rest on May 23, 1897. They gave him the largest funeral in the camp's history. Saloons, stores, and offices closed and people came from all over the country to take a last look at the man, who had found a mountain of silver worth $85,000,000.

Schieffelin Monument

The town of Tombstone was built on a flat mesa (called Goose Flats), surrounded by the Whetstone, Mule, Burro, Huachuca, and Dragoon Mountains. Early in 1879, Allen Street lots sold for $5 each and the town had 40 cabins and a population of 100.

Tombstone was to become the richest, gaudiest, the most lawless, wicked, and violent boomtown in the west. Gigantic ore wagons drawn by teams of 16 or 20 mules or horses, and carrying fortunes in high grade ore, formed a continuous parade the lengths of Allen and Fremont Streets, rumbling and creaking their way to and from the mills on the San Pedro River.

The first people who arrived in Tombstone were not land owners but squatters. Federal law required that the citizens incorporate as a town-site company, then they were to make a survey of the proposed town site, and then a temporary municipal government had to be established under territorial law.

When this had been done, the new officers then had to petition the Department of Interior for a patent for the federally owned land that was the intended town-site. Once this patent from the government was valid the new mayor would then be empowered to issue deeds to the people who already occupied the land. Any land not claimed at that time could be held by the city and sold to any who desired the property.

On March 5, 1879, five men organized the Tombstone Townsite Company. They were Anson P.K. Safford, Thomas J. Bidwell, Samuel Calhoun, James S. Clark, and Joseph C. Palmer. The latter two were politicians who had a lot of difficulty with the truth and honesty.

They surveyed 320 acres on "Goose Flats" which was to be the town site. The company then filed the proper town site claim. It was recorded at the U.S. Land Office in Florence on April 19, 1879. On April 22, 1879, it was recorded in the Pima County Recorder's Office.

One rather slippery character, named Mike Gray, bought

out Bidwell, Calhoun, Palmer, and Safford. Now Clark and Gray owned the company.

The first city election was held on November 24, 1879, with William M. Harwood being elected as mayor. Fred White, a 31 year old native of New York, was appointed Town Marshal. (MOST THINK THAT WHITE WAS AN OLD MAN WHEN HE WAS APPOINTED, BUT HE WAS ONLY 32 WHEN HE WAS KILLED.) Some weeks later in January, 1880, Alder Randall, a councilman, replaced William Harwood as mayor. Mike Gray was appointed City Clerk. The City Council applied for a patent to the town site, which was to be comprised of 2,394 lots. (Tombstone has always been troubled with selfish, dishonest people, but Clark, Gray and Randall were of the first order. Things have not changed.)

People became aware of the conspiracy on May 22, 1880, when Mayor Randall deeded 2,168 lots to Clark, Gray and Company for the incredible sum of $5.80. THAT IS ABOUT LIKE SELLING OUT FOR A STEAK DINNER AND COCKTAILS TODAY.) Ironically, this move transpired before the government issued the patent, which made it totally illegal. (LEGALITY IS NEVER A BIG CONCERN IN TOMBSTONE.)

Still, the members of the Town Lot Company, or their hirelings, would approach those who were already on city lots and offer to sell them clear title, which was usually much more than the lot was worth. If the people on the lot did not pay up, the Company sent members of the Cowboys to threaten and harass them.

These high handed tactics so angered the town's citizens that they organized a vigilante committee to protect the squatters. A public meeting was called in the San Jose House. Councilman Jones revealed evidence to those attending that bribery and corruption was rampant.

When word of this was spread around town tempers turned ugly. Their wrath was turned upon their Mayor, Alder Randall. That worthy, fearing that he might be strung up, departed for

Tucson in record time. However, on November 8, 1880, he got one last dirty trick on Tombstone, by signing a deed as mayor granting a large number of city lots to Clark, Gray, and Company.

On November 9, 1880, John Clum wrote in his Epitaph, "Tombstone has been handed over to the scheming speculators." (IT HAPPENED AGAIN IN 1994.)

After multiple lawsuits the Territorial Supreme Court made a final decision on July 8, 1886. The government had issued the patent on September 20, 1880, and the Court based their findings only on what happened after that date.

The decision that was handed down was that Randall had no legal right whatever to give title to any person or company except those who occupied the lots. Any profit to be derived from the lots not occupied was to go to the City of Tombstone. The conspiracy was labeled a legal and actual fraud.

When the outside world heard that Ed Schieffelin had found a mountain of silver, worth $85,000,000, in the middle of Apache country, newcomers flocked to the new boomtown in droves.

Tombstone was the last of the big boomtowns in the American West. Its first citizens were the last of the frontiers adventurers - colorful, brash, self-reliant, independent, tough...dangerous. Allen Street quickly became the most wicked street in the West. East of Sixth Street lay the red light district and west of Third Street lay Chinatown, called Hop Town by the local denizens. Prostitutes and narcotics could be had by all...for a price. The laughter of women could be heard all up and down Allen Street and the sweet odor of opium hung in the air. Chips clinked and roulette wheels whirred, followed by the cry, "Eight black!"

The people who were welcomed most in the wild and unruly camp were the red light women. It was quite natural that the women-starved men welcomed these painted ladies with wild celebrations. Their presence and fancy houses added a bit of refinement to the rough camp. The women themselves offered pleasure, amusement, and companionship to the lonely men, as it would be sometime before the respectable women would begin to arrive.

Some of these gaudy women were part-time entertainers, hoping to strike it rich; others were simply ladies of joy, who thoroughly enjoyed their line of work, each trying to make enough for security before age thwarted them; others were just obviously mercenary; and yet others were prostitutes because they saw no other avenue to survival.

It was really a shame-all those girls gone bad. We are referring to those women of the west, who followed the boomtowns, practicing the world's oldest profession. Of course, these women were judged as sinful, but some of them had no other choice.

During those difficult times there were no food stamps, welfare, free medical attention, or any other government assistance programs. Most folks had little knowledge of government or it of them. (We should have kept it that way.) Each individual was compelled to accept responsibility for his or her own survival or not. However, the men and women of that time were proud, rugged and independent individuals, and most found a way to survive.

Still a woman of that period was in dire need of a man-father, brother, or husband-to take care of her. There were very few exceptions to this fact. There were few jobs open to women; i.e. seamstress, cook, or laundress. And jobs such as these paid the very lowest wages.

Such conditions forced many young women, with no man in evidence, to make a choice between suicide and scandal. Many "boothills" of the old West contain the remains of those who chose suicide, but the red light district claimed a fair share of them too. Those who chose this line of endeavor were assured of survival-at least for an indefinite period-with some sort of income, however meager it might be. True, it was a tough, mer

Some of the girls who inhabited Sixth Street

ciless existence, but better than ending it all.

Most women quickly discovered that when men greatly out-number the women, any female who has a ready smile and pleasant personality and shows a spirit of cooperation in bestowing her sexual favors, could just about name her own price for those favors.

Usually there were two types of dwellings that served as "houses of ill repute"-the crib and the fancy parlour house. Because of local restrictions both were usually located in the same neighborhood, sometimes side by side, though there was a vast difference between the two.

The cribs were simply tiny buildings, usually ten feet by eight feet in size and constructed of rough lumber with a tin roof. Furniture normally consisted of one straight backed chair, a tiny table on which a washbowl sat, a single iron bed, a bot-tle of carbolic acid, and a small trunk for clothing. Cribs were single operations conducted by the prostitutes, who were in business for themselves. Their efforts were designed in such a fashion to promote the quick turnover principle so that the prostitute could spend as little time as possible with each cus-tomer.

Rent on such accommodations as these cost the prostitute about three dollars a day-paid in advance. This small area was where she lived as well as where she conducted her business.

The cribs were the lowest and most disreputable place to work. In Tombstone, prices for these women were set in a strange pattern: Chinese, Negro and Indian - 25¢; Mexican - 50¢; French - 75¢; and American - $1.00. These prices would change depending on age, beauty, or special abilities.

Disease, alcoholism, or drug addiction was their destiny in life. Very few "crib women" escaped this cruel fate. When asked about retirement, one worn prostitute replied, "Death is the only retirement from prostitution."

Most of Tombstone's parlour houses were at least two sto-ries-sometimes three. The lower floor was usually a saloon where a man might drink, dance, and gamble as much as it pleased him. In the upper parlour or parlours, girls and private rooms were available for those who tired of the entertainment provided on the first floor-at a price, of course. The rooms inside were elaborately and lavishly decorated with carved furniture, red velvet drapes, full length mirrors, exotic paintings, and deep, soft rugs. Young attractive maids and an uniformed butler served the customers on the first floor.

Most of the parlour houses had a standard fee that was about $10.00 with an all night charge of up to $30.00. Young girls with exceptional beauty could demand higher prices. So could older women who possessed special skills or a well known passionate ability. Each house could realize up to $150 a week. (Local miners were making three dollars for a twelve hour shift.)

The hours of house operation were usually from noon to daybreak each day. The women were given one day a week off. Big profit makers for the parlour houses were beer, whiskey, wine, and champagne. Customers were charged one dollar for a beer or a shot of whiskey; three dollars for a bottle of sour Mexican wine, and five dollars for a bottle of champagne.

Tombstone, as in other boomtowns, accepted prostitution as a necessary evil, a business that had to be regulated and rigidly controlled. It was perfectly legal to keep a "house of ill fame" in Tombstone as long as the appropriate city license was secured and the fees paid on a regular basis. Professional ladies were restricted from any form of public solicitation except in designated areas-dance halls and saloons. Quite often the streets that served as home and work place to these women were labeled as "Maiden Lane" or "Virgin Alley."

By Feb, 1880, Wells Spicer, local lawyer, wrote that Tombstone had two dance halls, a dozen gambling houses, over twenty saloons and more than 500 gamblers, but that there was still hope as he knew of two bibles in town.

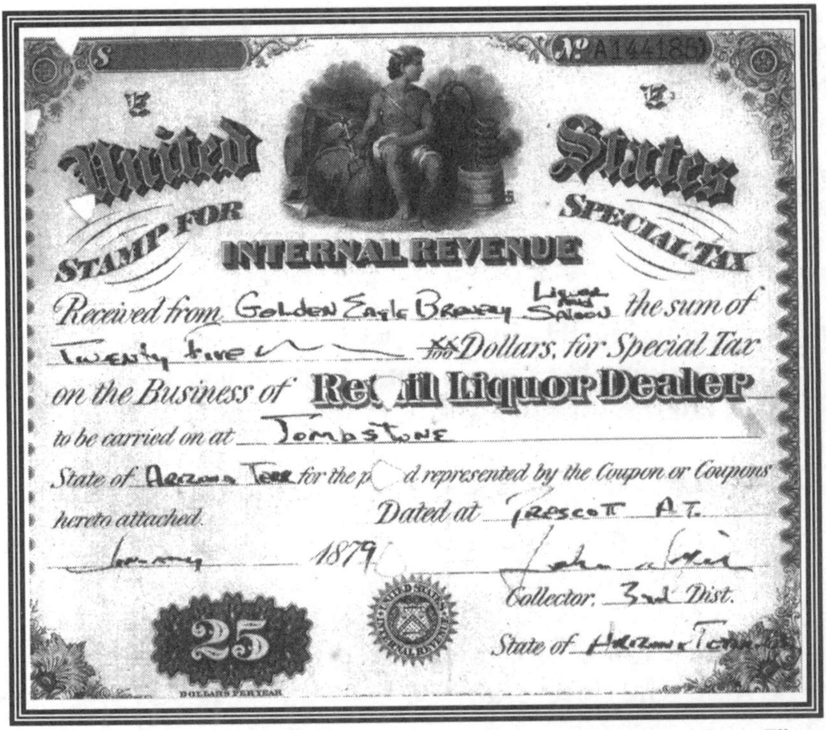
№ A144185
United States
Stamp for Special Tax
INTERNAL REVENUE
Received from Golden Eagle Brewery Liquor and Saloon the sum of Twenty five xx/100 Dollars, for Special Tax on the Business of Ret[illegible]il Liquor Dealer
to be carried on at Tombstone
State of Arizona Terr for the p[illegible]d represented by the Coupon or Coupons hereto attached.
Dated at Prescott A.T.
January 1879
Collector. 3rd Dist.
State of Arizona Terr
25
DOLLARS PER YEAR

Courtesy of Steve Elliott

CHAPTER I.

THEY CAME TO TOMBSTONE

"Old Man" Clanton, as he was called, was really Newman Haynes Clanton, born in Davidson County, Tennessee in 1816. He married Mariah Kelso, daughter of John and Mary Kelso, in Calloway County, Missouri, on January 5, 1840.

The Clanton family began farming in Calloway County and their first three children - John Wesley (1841); Phineas Fay (1845); and Joseph Isaac (1847); were born there. In 1852 they moved to Adams County, Illinois and their first daughter, Mary Elsie (1852) was born there.

The family moved again in 1853, this time to a farm in the vicinity of Dallas, Texas. Here they farmed and ran a few head of cattle. Two more children were born at this location; Esther Ann (1854) and Alonzo (1859).

Newman felt the urge to move frequently and he felt it again in 1861. This move was to Hamilton County, Texas, a violent and sparsely settled area with a large number of hostile Indians.

Newman Haynes and his oldest son, John Wesley, served in the Confederate Army - both enlisting as many times as they could without being caught - for the bonus money.

The Clanton's last child, William Harrison (1862), was born in Hamilton County.

When the war ended in 1865, the Clantons, strong, unbending Southerners, lost no time in moving west. On September 3, 1865, they were at Fort Bowie, Arizona and

(Larry Beyers photo)

Newman Haynes Clanton

Born Davidson County, Tennessee, 1816. Known as "Old Man." Killed by Doc Holliday in Guadalupe Canyon, Mexico on August 13, 1881.)

Joseph Isaac Clanton
(Fly Photo)

Ike was the individual that caused most of the trouble. He involved all his family, that was near him, in his problems. He instigated the gunfight at O.K. Corral, then ran away. When he was killed by J.V. Brighton on June 1, 1887 the Apache County critic said, "Thus ended the wild career of poor deluded, misguided Ike Clanton. He 'sowed to the wind and has harvested the whirlwind,' and his harvest is gathered into a narrow house, six feet by two."

were described thusly: Newman, 6 feet, 1 inch, fair complexion, light hair and blue eyes; John Wesley, 5 feet, 11 inches, fair complexion, light hair and brown eyes; Phineas, 5 feet, 8 inches, fair complexion with brown hair and blue eyes.

By 1877, some of the older children had moved elsewhere. Mariah had died in 1866. "Old Man" and his sons, Phineas, Ike, and Billy moved to southeast Arizona. They took up land at Lewis Springs about five miles south of Charleston and about twelve miles from Tombstone (not yet built). Here on a hilltop, the Clantons built a large, thick-walled adobe house that afforded them a complete view in all directions. No one could approach without being seen a long way off.

The Arizona Weekly Star, December, 1878, made mention that Ike Clanton had opened a restaurant at the Tombstone Mill Site. Many have placed this location at Tombstone or Watervale, when actually the Tombstone Mill Site was at Millville on the San Pedro.

With all this activity, the Clantons prospered. Before long, two young men, Tom and Frank McLaury, moved in nearby and started a ranch. The two newcomers and the Clantons soon became friends and on infrequent occasions did business together.

The McLaury brothers were from a respected family, and it is difficult to see how they became involved with the Clantons.

Robert Houston McLaury (1811-1893) and Margaret Rowland McLaury (1812-1859) had eleven children: Ebenezer (1833); Margaret Findley (1836); Hugh (1838); Edmund (1840); Mary (1842); William Rowland (1844); Marjorie Agnes (1846); Robert Findley (this was Frank) (1848); Christiana (1851); Thomas Clark (1853); and Sarah Caroline(1855).

Robert Findley and Tom were born in Korthright, New York. William Rowland always seemed to be closer to Tom and Frank than the other children. He and Edmund served in Union Army; Edmund, dying of exposure, while a prisoner of war, on October 14, 1862.

Hassell,

Robert Findley McLaury

Born in Korthright, New York in 1848. Killed in the O.K. Corral gunfight on October 26, 1881. He is buried in Tombstone's Boothill.

Hassell.

Thomas Clark McLaury

Born in Korthright, New York in 1853. Killed in the Gunfight at O.K. Corral by a shotgun blast from Doc Holliday on October 26, 1881. He is buried in Tombstone's Boothill.

Following the war William moved to Vermillion, South Dakota to practice law. From there he moved to Fort Worth, Texas, where he maintained a law practice until 1901. Frank and Tom visited with him in 1878 on their way to Arizona. They arrived in Arizona Territory in 1879 settling in the San Pedro Valley near the Clanton ranch. Building a small cabin, they began the business of building a herd of cattle.

About the same time period a rustler's trail was defined as running from "Old Man" Clanton's ranch northeast close by Tombstone; through South Pass in the Dragoon Mountains, to Soldier's Hole in the Sulphur Springs Valley, to Rustler's Park in the Chiricahuas and on to Galeyville on their eastern slope, down to the Animas Valley in New Mexico and to the Mexican border.

"Old Man" Clanton and Curly Bill Brocius were the leaders of the outlaws, who were engaged in the robbery and rustling on both sides of the border. As the McLaury brothers became full-fledged gang members, they would soon become involved in the confrontation with the law and order people.

Ringo! It is truly a magic, romantic name. The mere sound of it brings to the imagination visions of steely-eyed gunmen wreathed in flame and gunsmoke. Ringo! The deadliest and most feared gunfighter in all the West!

Not quite! That statement is most inaccurate. He was NEVER, EVER involved in a real gunfight. He was involved in some very real cold-blooded killings in Texas and Arizona, but in no instance where his victims had the means and the opportunity to defend themselves. The truth of the matter is - if his name had been Baumgardiner we would never have heard of him!

John Peters Ringo was not born in Texas, or Missouri, or California as many claim. He was born on March 3, 1850, in Green Fork, Indiana. He was the eldest born to Martin Albert and Mary Peters. The others were Martin Albert, Jr., born January 28, 1854; Fanny Fern, born July 20, 1857; Mary

Enna, born May 2, 1860; and Mattie Bell, born April 28, 1862.

Ringo became involved in the "Hoodoo" war in Texas; a range war between German and American families. The law began to come down on him and he fled Texas with a cohort, named Joe Hill. They must have stopped off in New Mexico. At least they were there long enough for Joe Hill to get his name on the wanted list published by Governor Lew Wallace.

When these two desperadoes arrived in Arizona Territory, Tombstone was still a part of Pima County, ruled by outlaws and known as a haven for any man with a price on his head.

Ringo and Hill were quickly welcomed into the ranks of the Cowboy gang, and, because of that association, he was to become an arch enemy of the Earp brothers and Doc Holliday. It did not take Ringo long to come before the public eye again. In the Mormon town of Safford, on December 9, 1879, he shot Lewis Hancock for refusing a drink. Hancock was unarmed.

The Tucson Star, December 14, 1879, carried the following account:

"Last Tuesday night a shooting affair took place in which Lewis Hancock was shot by John Ringo. It appears Ringo wanted Hancock to take a drink and he refused saying he would prefer a beer. Ringo struck him over the head with the pistol and then fired, the ball taking effect in the lower end of the left ear, and passed through the fleshy part of the neck. Half an inch more in the neck would have killed him. Ringo is under arrest."

Meanwhile, others were on their way to Tombstone, others, who would not be friendly to the Clantons or the McLaurys or Ringo. They were the Earp brothers. Nicholas Porter Earp (1813-1907) and his second wife, Virginia Ann Cooksey (1823-1893) were married in 1840. Their union produced five sons and three daughters; James Cooksey (1841-1926); Virgil Walter (1843-1906); Martha Elizabeth (1845-1856); Wyatt Berry Stapp (1848-1929); Morgan S. (1851-1882); Warren

Baxter (1855-1900); Virginia Ann (1858-1861); Adelia Douglas (1861-1941).

Old Nick's first wife, Abigail Storm (1813-1839) gave him a son, named Newton Jasper (1837-1928). Newton, James, and Virgil all served in the Union Army during the War of Northern Aggression. James was wounded so severely that he was partially disabled the remainder of his life. The brothers were quite clannish, and where you found one of them you eventually found the others, with the exception of Newton, the half brother.

James Earp, eldest of the full brothers, enlisted in Company F, Seventeenth Illinois Infantry, was wounded at Fredricktown, Missouri on October 3, 1861, and was discharged from disability on March 22, 1863. Since he had little use of his left arm, he drew a disability pension the rest of his life. James was a gambler, saloon-keeper, store-keeper and sometime hack driver. He married Nellie Bartlett Ketchum (Bessie) on April 18, 1873. James landed the first Earp job in Tombstone-tending bar at Vogan's; working there until he opened the Sampling Room in 1881. Many said he was the best-liked of the Earp brothers. His physical condition kept him from becoming involved in their escapades.

Virgil Earp was described as: "A bold, daring man with blond hair, smoky blue eyes and a sinister expression; he is not a man to trifle with." At about 17 years, Virgil began to court Ellen Rysdam, a 15 year old daughter of a Dutch neighbor. They eventually ran away and got married. Nicholas and the old Dutch man were outraged at this untimely and unexpected marriage, and separated the young couple until their union could be annulled.

As his father and father-in-law would not let him live with his wife, Virgil enlisted in the Union Army, 83rd Illinois Infantry, Company C at Monmouth on August 21, 1862.

All through the war he believed that Ellen waited for him to return. Unknown to him Ellen thought he was dead. Virgil was

Virgil Walter Earp

Born in Hartford, Kentucky on July 18, 1843. Served in the Union Army, 83rd Illinois Infantry, Company C during the War Between the States. Lived with Alvira Sullivan for 32 years, but is doubtful they were married. Wounded in the Gunfight at O.K. Corral and on the streets of Tombstone two months later. Served as Tombstone Town Marshal and Deputy U.S. Marshal. Was the first Marshal of Colton, California. Died in Goldfield, Nevada on October 19, 1905.

Glenn Boyer Photo

Glenn Boyer Photo

Alvira Sullivan Earp

Born near Council Bluffs, Nebraska, on January 4, 1849. She was barely five feet tall and Irish. She lived with Virgil for 32 years. She died in Los Angeles on November 14, 1947, almost 99 years of age.

mustered out in Nashville on June 26, 1865. When he reached home he was appalled to find that not only his young wife had disappeared, but his own family as well. Ellen and her family had moved to an unknown destination in the Pacific Northwest. Virgil lost all contact with the girl to whom he had been briefly married. Many years later he discovered that they had a daughter.

In 1869, Virgil and Wyatt found that the rest of the family was living in Lamar, Missouri where Nick's brother Jonathan lived. While they were there Virgil married a woman named Rozilla Dragoo, and Wyatt married Urilla Sutherland. Wyatt's wife died of a fever later that year. There is no record of what happened to Virgil's wife. She seems to have disappeared. It is likely that she was a track follower.

Virgil rode out of Missouri alone. He reached Council Bluffs, Iowa in 1873. Sometime after that he met Alvira Sullivan. She was Irish, born and raised in Nebraska. They were soon living together, traveling through Nebraska, Wyoming, Colorado and Kansas finally settling near Prescott, Arizona. In 1877, Virgil became a deputy sheriff, and on November 5, 1878, he was elected Constable for the Prescott Precinct in the County of Yavapai.

Two cowboys once shot up the town and a posse was sent to round them up. Virgil was a member of the posse and in trying to arrest the cowboys, shot and killed one of them.

Virgil began to feel that it was time for a change, so he wrote to his brother, Wyatt, from Prescott, advising him to leave Dodge City and go to Tombstone as there appeared to be unlimited opportunities in the new silver camp.

Feeling that he would need some sort of job in Tombstone, Virgil talked U.S. Marshall Crawley Dake into making him a deputy U.S. Marshal. Dake appointed him and his commission was filed with the Federal Commissions Office in Tucson on November 27, 1879. Virgil and Alvira (Allie) arrived in Tombstone the last of November.

(Glenn Boyer photo)

Wyatt Berry Stapp Earp

Born March 19, 1848, in Monmouth, Illinois. Served as a law-man, in Missouri, Kansas, and Arizona. Named after his father's commanding officer in the Mexican War. Killed most of the men responsible for the death of Morgan and the crippling of Virgil. Died in Los Angeles on January 13, 1929.

Wyatt Earp was described as cold and calculating, and the brains behind his brothers. While he was residing in Lamar, he ran for constable against his half brother, Newton, and won. When his wife died he moved on and in May, 1872, he was arrested for horse stealing. He put up bail, but ran out on it. His partner in crime, Edward Kennedy, had his case dismissed.

For a few years Wyatt worked for a survey party, freighting, buffalo hunting, and various other occupations. In April, 1875, he was appointed to the Wichita Police force. On three different occasions: May 17 to September 9, 1876; July 6 to November, 1877; and May 12, 1878 to September 8, 1879; he was an officer in Dodge City.

Sometime during these latter years, Wyatt met a woman, named Celia Ann Blaylock. She was born in Fairfax, Iowa in January, 1850. Wyatt probably found her in Fort Scott, Kansas. She was a prostitute, picked up along the way by Wyatt, and she answered to the nickname of Mattie.

Wyatt, tired of Dodge City, left for Tombstone in September, 1879. Mattie, who had been living with him, rode along. Also in this party of travelers were James Earp, his wife, Bessie and her daughter, Hattie.

When Wyatt, James, and their wives reached Prescott, they met John Henry "Doc" Holliday and his sometime lady friend, Big Nose Kate.

John Henry Holliday was born into the South in that wonderful time before the War Between the States (August 14, 1851). It was the time of the grand plantations and the verandahs were scented by the sweet blossoms of magnolia, jasmine, and honeysuckle. As was customary, plantation families took their places as leaders in the social and political patterns of Dixie. These positions were entirely due to wealth, education, and family bloodlines. John Henry came into this world as a blue-blood of this society-endowed with all the natural inheritances of a son of the South.

Celia Ann Blaylock

Born in Fairfax, Iowa in January, 1850, she met Wyatt Earp in Fort Scott, Kansas. She was a prostitute, called Mattie, that Wyatt lived with for a number of years. He deserted her after Tombstone. She committed suicide in Pinal, Arizona, on July 3, 1888, by taking an overdose of laudanum (opium) and whiskey.

(Glenn Boyer photo)

(Boyer collection photo)

Big Nose Kate

(1890 photo)

She was Doc Holliday's woman - sometimes. She was born in Budapest Hungary in 1850. Died in the Pioneer's Home in Prescott, Arizona November 2, 1940. She was using the name Mary K. Cummings. Almost 90 years of age.

John Henry Holliday

(at 21 years)

Born August 14, 1851, in Griffin, Georgia. Graduated from the Pennsylvania College of Dental Surgery in Philadelphia on March 1, 1872, with the Degree of Doctor of Dental Surgery. He died of tuberculosis at the Hotel Glenwood, Glenwood Springs, Colorado on November 8, 1887.

(From painting by Mike James)

Great dramatic changes were soon to come about in the life of young Holliday-changes that certainly did much to mold his personality into what it finally became.

In 1865, Southern society was destroyed forever. The Confederacy surrendered and the occupation began. It was a thinly veiled plot to systematically loot the South. It became a very difficult time for all proud, hot-tempered Southerners.

But, in September, 1866, the worst blow of all struck young John. His beloved mother died and changed his way of life forever. More ill fortune was to come his way. John attended dental college in Philadelphia and soon after graduation, was told that he had incurable tuberculosis, and only a short time to live! Can you imagine the effects of these monstrous calamities in the life of a young man just 21 years old?

Many "sensational" writers have Holliday killing men he never saw in places he never was, killing men that were actually killed by someone else, and even some that were not killed at all.

In the fall of 1877, Doc was to meet Kate Elder, known as Big Nose Kate, in Fort Griffin, Texas. She was the woman who was to be the only female ever heavily involved with him. Kate had been born in Budapest and was as well educated as Holliday.

In Doc's new surroundings out west, everyone went armed with a gun or a knife - many with several. Doc was certainly not physically able to stand up to such opponents, who had little regard for life or limb, on a strength basis. Therefore, in order to compensate for his physical deficiencies, he taught himself every aspect of defense with pistol and knife. It was not long until he was well known for his ability with weapons and a deck of cards, as well as his legendary consumption of whiskey.

Doc also met another person in Fort Griffin in November, 1877, who would have a great impact on his life; Wyatt Earp. Earp had been trailing Dave Rudabaugh, but had lost the trail. He had ridden into Fort Griffin in the hopes that someone

James Cooksey Earp

Born June 28, 1841, Hartford, Kentucky. Served in the Union Army, 17th Illinois Infantry, Company F. Wounded and crippled for life at Fredericktown, Missouri on October 3, 1861. Married Nellie Bartlett Ketchum, called Bessie, on April 18, 1873. He died in Los Angeles on January 25, 1926.

(Glenn Boyer photo)

(Glenn Boyer photo)

Nellie (Bessie) Bartlett Ketchum Earp
Wife of James

could tell him Rudabaugh's whereabouts.

At the Bee Hive, John Shanssey said that Doc Holliday might tell him where Rudabaugh had gone to ground. Holliday agreed to find the information for Wyatt, but only because he felt that he owed John Shanssey a favor. By the time he had found that Rudabaugh was hiding down in the vicinity of Fort Davis, Doc and Wyatt had become friends, a friendship that would last all of Doc's life.

Bat Masterson did not like Holliday and he said:

"Holliday had a mean disposition and an ungovernable temper, and under the influence of liquor, was a most dangerous man."

In 1877, Doc was described as being a slim, young man, five feet, ten inches tall, and weighing about 140 pounds, with blond hair, piercing blue eyes, and a large blond mustache.

By this time Doc was becoming widely known as the "deadly dentist." Most of his killer reputation had been gained by the stories Doc, himself, had told about the numerous people that he had shot down. This awesome reputation was his defense mechanism. Though his bloody deeds were told in detail, he killed no one in Georgia, Texas, Colorado, Wyoming, South Dakota, Kansas, or New Mexico. Doc Holliday killed no men anywhere except Arizona.

When he met Wyatt and James in Prescott, he was on his way to Tombstone, too, but was having a run of luck at the gaming tables and declined to go with the Earp party saying, "I'll be along a little later."

James, Wyatt, and their wives arrived in Tombstone on December 1, 1879 and set up camp in Virgil's yard. Before he had left Dodge City, Wyatt had written to Morgan in Montana and told him that the other brothers were going to Tombstone. When Morgan and his wife, Louisa, had received the news, they decided to go, too.

(Glenn Boyer photo)

Morgan S. Earp

Born in Pella, Iowa on April 24, 1851. Worked as a lawman and Wells Fargo guard. Wounded in the Gunfight at O.K. Corral. Murdered in Campbell & Hatch's Saloon in Tombstone on March 18, 1882.

Louisa Houston Earp

Born in Wisconsin, she was the granddaughter of Sam Houston. She lived with Morgan Earp from 1879 until he was killed in Tombstone. She died in Long Beach on June 12, 1894.

(Glenn Boyer photo)

(Glenn Boyer photo)

Morgan Earp was known as the most handsome and the most reckless of the Earp brothers. The "Brother in the Shadow," as Glenn Boyer, the dean of Earp historians, refers to him, did not make all the moves around the country that the rest of the family did. He did go to California with them in 1864 and returned to Pella, Iowa with them in 1868. No mention has been made of him being in Lamar.

However, Morgan did do some work as a process server for Sheriff Charles Bassett in Dodge City in 1875. Apparently, it was during that time that he met Louisa Houston, a granddaughter of Sam Houston. Her father had been born of Sam Houston and a Cherokee woman, out of wedlock.

She used the name Louisa Earp, though it seems she did it reluctantly, and there is no evidence to prove that she and Morgan were legally married. At any rate, they were living together in Butte, Montana in 1879. Louisa was a very beautiful young woman - easily the loveliest of all the Earp women.

There is no evidence to date that Wyatt ever married Mattie or Josie; Virgil ever married Allie, or that Morgan married Louisa.

In December, 1879, the "Pinafore on Wheels" troupe arrived in Tombstone. One of the cast members was a beautiful Jewish girl from San Francisco, named Josephine Sarah Marcus. She would leave soon, but she would return the next year to cause more than her share of trouble.

John Phillip Clum arrived in Tombstone the first time in December, 1879. Clum had gone to Rutgers College and was a member of the Dutch Reformed Church. He was working for the Signal Corps, when his classmates volunteered him for the job of Indian Agent at the San Carlos Reservation. In this position he was the only man to ever capture Geronimo. If the United States government had paid heed to the 25 year old Indian agent, John Clum, and hanged the murderer, Geronimo, when Clum captured that wily Apache, and delivered him into their hands, 500 human lives and $12,000,000 would not have been forfeited and the Apache Wars would have ended in

1877, not 1886!

Unable to accept governmental policies concerning the Apache, Clum resigned in July, 1877. He and his wife bought a newspaper, "The Arizona Citizen," and moved to Florence. This was the first newspaper in Pinal County, Arizona (November 16, 1877).

In February, 1879, the Clums moved to Tucson and established the "Daily Arizona Citizen." This was the first daily newspaper published in Arizona Territory.

While visiting Tombstone, Clum liked what he saw and on February 2, 1880, he decided to found the "Tombstone Epitaph" with Charles Reppy as his business partner. Many, many people criticized the name he chose for his newspaper, but he was adamant, and replied, "Every tombstone should have an epitaph." His newspaper still exists in the "town too tough to die."

The first edition of the Epitaph was released on May 1, 1880. Clum's front page editorial, "The First Trumpet" said: "Tombstone is a city upon a hill promising to vie with ancient Rome upon her seven hills in a fame different in character but no less in importance."

Clum was to become a staunch supporter of the law and order party and the Earps. He also became the Postmaster, Mayor, Chairman of the School Trustee, and Sir Knight Commander of the Knights of Pythias.

Warren Baxter Earp

Born March 9, 1855, at Pella, Iowa. Took part in some of the Tombstone troubles. Killed by John Boyett in Willcox Arizona on July 6, 1900. He was the youngest of the Earp brothers.

(Glenn Boyer photo)

Earp Property:

Date	Locators	Claim Name
12-6-1879	Virgil, Wyatt, James, Robert Winders	1st North Ext. Mountain Maid
12-10-1879	Same as above	Earp
1-14-1880	Same as above and A.S. Neff	Grasshopper
2-8-1880	Virgil, Wyatt, James	Dodge
2-16-1880	Same as above	Mattie Blaylock
2-16-1880	Wyatt and A.S. Neff	Comstock
2-21-1880	Virgil, Wyatt, James, and A.S. Neff	Rocky Ridge
4-20-1880	Wyatt Earp	Long Branch
11-4-1880	C. Billicke, Wyatt, Albert Steinfield	The Bull
11-4-1880	Virgil Earp	Red Star

Property Block	Lot Numbers	Taxpayers
29	22	Earp bros. & Winders
V	3	James Earp
29	23	Virgil Earp
29	24	James Earp
29	1	Virgil & Winders
29	2	Wyatt & James
M	1	Winders & Virgil
M	2	Same as above
M	3	James Earp
M	4	Wyatt Earp

CHAPTER II

BOOMTOWN LIFE

Soon after arriving in Tombstone, the Earps filed on several mining claims and managed to acquire a number of city lots. Wyatt also developed interests in some gambling layouts and was soon employed as a guard for Wells Fargo.

All the Earps settled on Fremont Street. Wyatt and Mattie on the northeast corner of Fremont and First Streets; Virgil and Allie on the southwest corner of the same location. Jim and Bessie lived just up Fremont from Virgil and Allie.

Early in 1880, another main character showed in Tombstone. John Harris Behan was born in Westport (Kansas City), Missouri on October 23, 1845 to Peter Behan and Sarah Ann Harris, who had a total of 14 children. Little is known of John's childhood, except that he received a better education than most at that time.

When he grew up he had serious difficulty dealing with the problems along the Kansas-Missouri boarder. Even his mother and father had violent disagreements over the slavery issue. Young Behan got away from it by just heading west in 1863; first going to San Francisco, then to Prescott, Arizona Territory.

Early in 1866 he was involved in several skirmishes with the Apaches. Later, on October 8, 1866, he was appointed deputy sheriff of Yavapai County; in October, 1867 he became the under-sheriff, and in 1871 he became Yavapai County Sheriff. Behan was elected the county recorder on June 20, 1868. At other times he was the tax collector, district court deputy clerk, and assessor.

John Harris Behan

Born in Westport, Missouri on October 23, 1845. First sheriff, Cochise County, Arizona. Took office on February 1, 1881. Later became superintendent of the Territorial Prison at Yuma on April 1, 1888. During the Spanish-American War he served as a civilian quartermaster in Cuba. Served in the quartermaster capacity during the Boxer Rebellion in China in 1900. His last job was as head of the Commissary Department of the Arizona Eastern Railroad. Behan died at St. Mary's Hospital in Tucson on June 7, 1912. He is buried in the Holy Hope Cemetery in Tucson.

(Talei Publishers photo)

Nashville Frank Leslie

Claimed to have been born in Galveston, Texas in 1842. Worked as a bartender in the Oriental Saloon; sometimes under-cover for Wells Fargo. Killed Killeen, Claibourne, and Blonde Mollie. Disappeared when released from Yuma Pen.

In March, 1869, he married a woman named Victoria Zaffin of San Francisco. They had two children, Henrietta, born in 1869, and Albert, born in 1871. Henrietta died very young, only living five years.

Victoria divorced him in 1875. Behan was charged with openly visiting houses of ill fame and prostitution and specifically having sexual intercourse with a prostitute called Sadie. The judge granted the divorce.

By May, 1878 Behan was back into the political arena, running for sheriff of Mojave County. It was one of the few times he was not victorious in politics. But, he rebounded by being elected to the Tenth Legislature Assembly from Mojave County in 1879.

John Behan left Prescott in October, 1879, to accept the job of deputy sheriff at Gillett. It was while he was with a posse from this office chasing Mexican stage robbers that he met the person who was to drastically change his life; Josephine Marcus. This young lady from San Francisco had run away from home to join a traveling show. Behan's posse escorted the troupe into Prescott.

Early in the year 1880, Behan moved to Tombstone, where he secured employment as a bartender at the Grand Hotel. Later, he was to form a partnership with John Dunbar in a livery stable called the Dexter, located across Allen Street from the O.K. Corral.

On May 12, 1880, Josephine Marcus, the dark eyed Jewish beauty from San Francisco, returned to Tombstone and registered at the Cosmopolitan Hotel. She soon made it known that she had come to town to marry John Behan. She said that they had met when she was traveling through Arizona with the "Pinafore on Wheels" troupe, and that Johnny had later visited her in San Francisco, and, in her words, convinced her to come to Tombstone with a promise of marriage.

It was not long until Behan and Josie moved into a small house on the corner of Seventh and Safford Streets. Behan's ten year old son, Albert, lived with them. Josie liked the boy, a product of Behan's first marriage, and they became fast friends. Soon, Johnny said no more about marriage.

Doc Holliday was listed on the Census of Inhabitants in Prescott, Yavapai County on June 3, 1880. So he and Kate arrived in Tombstone after that.

Big Nose Kate, Horony, Fisher, Melvin, Elder, Holliday, Cummings of Tombstone fame was a very elusive mystery until a few years ago when Glenn Boyer unraveled the tangled web of her life.

Kate was what she was and she made no excuses about it - she was Big Nose Kate - a dance hall woman and prostitute at times. True, her nose was prominent, but her other attributes were quite attractive. Her curves were generous, well rounded, and in the right places. Tough, fearless, high tempered, and stubborn, Kate was a prostitute whenever she wanted because she was prone to do whatever she wanted at any time. She belonged to no man and served no madam, but operated as an individual in any manner she chose whenever the mood struck her.

When Doc left Prescott for Tombstone, Kate had been quite happy to go along as Doc left with several thousand dollars of Prescott gamblers' money in his pockets.

The only living accommodations that Doc could find for the two of them was an empty room between the funeral parlor and the Soma Winery on the north side of Allen Street just above Sixth Street. (The tennis courts stand there now.)

Once they were settled in, Holliday and Kate took up where they had left off. Though they lived together, life was a constant battle of arguing and bickering. Doc went back to drinking and gambling and Kate to her operations of doing whatever pleased her.

The Cowboys had had things their way in Tombstone for quite some time and they resented the presence of the Earp brothers and Holliday. The Earps considered Doc a welcome addition to their fight with the Cowboy faction.

Doc was famous as a "badman" when he arrived in Tombstone, although he had not killed a single man at that time. Still, stories abounded that many men had died in front of his roaring guns. These wild tales had built him an awesome reputation. And not one person in Tombstone knew any better!

"Old Man" Clanton and three of his sons; Phin, Ike, and Billy, lost no time in letting Doc know that he had incurred their wrath and extreme displeasure by joining forces with the Earp brothers.

On a hot and dusty day in the early summer of 1880, a lithe, muscular man with a long, flowing, mustache, a fringed buckskin jacket, and a matched pair of six-guns, rode into Tombstone. This man was Nashville Franklyn Leslie, soon to be known as "Buckskin Frank." He was to stay in Tombstone nine years, and to write his name indelibly in the town's bloody history. Leslie was one of Tombstone's fastest guns, its most notorious ladies' man, and its biggest liar. (it is not known whether R.F. Coleman was considered for this latter title.)

Leslie was employed as a bartender in the Oriental Saloon. At one time the Oriental had so many fights, shootings, and knifings that it was closed down. (The City Council made Leslie a special officer with "power of arrest on the premises of the Oriental Saloon" on November 29, 1880.)

At a local dance one night, Leslie deserted the dance hall girls in favor of a black-haired beauty named May Killeen. May was separated from her husband, Mike, but he had made it known around town that he would shoot any man who showed her any attention. Leslie completely ignored such threats.

Apparently, "Buckskin Frank" was hopelessly captivated by the lovely May Killeen and, although Mike Killeen had personally warned him to stop seeing her, he paid no heed. Evidently May had some strong feelings about the handsome Leslie, too, as they were seen together frequently.

On the night of June 12, 1880, Mike Killeen, while working at his job as a bartender in the Commercial Hotel, heard someone remark that May was at the dance with Leslie. Mike left his job and went to the Cosmopolitan Hotel to wait for them. When the couple arrived, arm in arm, Killeen, overcome by unreasonable jealousy, rushed out and confronted them.

Guns roared in the darkness, and Killeen was fatally wounded. From this point on, all the accounts varied. Leslie and a man named George Perrine, who happened to be on the hotel back porch, were arrested and held until Killeen died. Since the dead man had publicly threatened to kill Leslie, no legal action was taken against him.

A few days after her husband had been conveniently buried in Boothill, the comely widow, May Killeen, married Frank Leslie. The new groom had difficulty adjusting to married life. He started drinking even more and, when drunk, his vile temper came out. Leslie could not confine himself to one woman, and the marriage was soon doomed.

Foremost among Tombstone's tales of violence is that of the gaudy shirt that led to murder. On July 24, 1880, T.J. Waters had been drinking in the Allen Street Saloons and had consumed enough to become evil tempered. Waters had bought himself a new shirt that day - one of black and blue plaid. Little did he realize that the brightly colored shirt would cause his death before sunset.

Many of the men on Whiskey Row made good natured comments about his new shirt. Somehow, this put him in a foul mood and he became very abusive.

"Now, if any man here don't like my shirt, let him get up. I'm chief. I'm boss here and I'll knock any man down who opens his mouth about my shirt again!"

E.L. Bradshaw came in Corrigan's Saloon (Alhambra) shortly after. He and Waters were friends and he had not heard the latter's words. Bradshaw smiled and commented on Waters' shirt. Without a word, Waters struck him a heavy blow above the left eye, knocking him unconscious.

When Bradshaw recovered from Waters' blow, he went back to his cabin and got his pistol. He located Waters, confronted him, and asked, "Why did you hit me?" Waters answered with a tirade of profanity and threats.

Bradshaw drew his pistol and shot Waters four times. One bullet entered under the left arm, piercing the heart, one through the top of the head, and the other two between the shoulder blades. Any one of the four shots would have been fatal.

Bradshaw was arrested, but the circumstances and the times being what they were, he went free. But fate was eventually to bring him to justice. In 1887, "Buckskin Frank" Leslie, who had a terrible reputation as Tombstone's most notorious ladies' man, decided that he wanted a new girlfriend. The one he chose was a shapely blond, named Mollie Williams. She was a song and dance girl at the Bird Cage and was known as Blonde Mollie. Her current boyfriend was none other than E.L. Bradshaw.

One morning, Bradshaw was found behind the Oriental Saloon with a bullet hole through his head. Many people in Tombstone believed that Leslie had killed him to get the luscious Mollie. Leslie never denied killing Bradshaw - but he never admitted it, either. Leslie also killed Blonde Mollie, too, but that is beyond the scope of this volume.

The first incident that caused a confrontation between the Earps and the Cowboys was the theft of six army mules from Camp Rucker. Virgil, Wyatt, and Morgan Earp, Marshall Williams, Lieutenant J.H. Hurst, and four soldiers tracked the stolen mules to McLaury's ranch on the Babocomari River near Fairbank. The date was July 25, 1880.

Dave Estes, in Charleston, told the posse that they would find the mules at the McLaury ranch; that he saw them branding the mules DS, making a DS out of the U.S. brand. They found the newly branded mules as well as the DS branding iron that had been used.

Frank Patterson made a deal with Lt. Hurst that if the Earps went back to Tombstone, then the Cowboys would turn over all the army mules to Hurst. Wyatt tried to tell Hurst it was a trick and that the thieves had no intention of returning the animals.

Hurst insisted so the posse returned to Tombstone. Sometime afterward Hurst told Wyatt that after the Earps had departed the Cowboys refused to give up the mules. They laughed at Hurst and said they only wanted to get rid of the Earps because they knew that the army wouldn't stand up to them. Hurst also cautioned the Earps about the Cowboys, saying that they had made threats against their lives.

During this incident Wyatt had no position as a lawman as he would not become a deputy sheriff for two more days. However, Virgil was a federal officer and the mules were federal property, so he was the leader of the posse.

Lieutenant Hurst printed an information placard and reward notice concerning the theft of the army mules in the Tombstone Epitaph, July 30, 1880. A copy of this notice is included in this book.

On August 5, 1880, a very angry Frank McLaury answered in the Tombstone Daily Nugget:

> *"On the morning of July 25, 1880, this man Hurst came to my ranch with an escort of soldiers accompanied by several citizens and he took me aside and told me, in substance, that he had had stolen from Camp Rucker six army mules, and stated that they were stolen by Pony Diehl, A.S. Hahsbrough and MacMasters(sic)...*
>
> *If J. H. Hurst was a gentleman, or if I could appeal to the courts for protection, I would proceed differently in this matter, but Hurst is irresponsible and I have but one course to pursue, and that is to publish to the world that J.H. Hurst, 1st Lieut. 12th Inft. A.A.Q.M. is a coward, a vagabond, a rascal, and a malicious liar. This base and unmanly action is the result of cowardice, for instead of hunting the stock himself he tried to get others to do it, and when they could not find it, in order to cover up his own wrong acts, he attempted*

to traduce the character and reputation of honest men.

My name is well known in Arizona and thank God that this is the first time in my life that the name of dishonesty was ever attached to me. Perhaps when the matter is ventilated it will be found that the Hon. Lieut. Hurst has stolen those mules and sold them, for a coward will steal, and a man who can publish the placard that bears his name is a coward. I am willing to let the people of Arizona decide who is right.

Frank McLaury
Babocomari, August 2, 1880."

Frank was just mouthing off here. It seems that the posse did very well in finding the stolen mules - right on Frank's property. It was ridiculous to accuse Hurst of the theft when they were obviously in the possession of the Cowboys.

The real truth of the matter is that Zwing Hunt, Billy Grounds, and Curly Bill stole the mules from Fort Rucker. Frank Patterson and the McLaurys were rebranding them and holding them until they could be sold. They were just caught red-handed in the act!

Sheriff Charley Shibell appointed Wyatt Earp a deputy sheriff of Pima County on July 27, 1880. The Epitaph commented:

"Wyatt has filled various positions in which bravery and determination were requisites, and in every instance proved himself the right man in the right place. He is at present filling the position of shotgun messenger for Wells Fargo & Co. which he will resign to accept the latter appointment. Morgan Earp succeeds his brother as shotgun messenger for Wells, Fargo & Co."

NO STAGE THAT ANY EARP WAS RIDING SHOTGUN ON WAS EVER HELD UP!

Morgan and Louisa, leaving Montana, reached Nick Earp's home in Colton in March, 1880. Morgan tarried there a while, then leaving Louisa with his parents, went on to Tombstone, arriving there the first week of July, 1880.

Tombstone received a large part of its bad reputation during the year 1880. George Parsons wrote in his journal the night of July 30, 1880:

> "Still another man killed - Wilson - shot dead this A.M. by King, an anti-Chinese agitator, who is at the head of a movement here to drive out the Chinese. Our town is getting a pretty hard reputation. Men killed every few days besides numerous pullings and firing of pistols and fist fights."

Thomas Wilson had been in Tombstone a few weeks, having arrived from San Francisco. Shortly after his arrival he had gone to work as a tin roofer.

Roger King, also a newcomer, had worked for a while at the Contention Mill, but had soon quit and then devoted full-time to being a trouble-maker.

Frank Leslie said that King showed up in the saloon at the Cosmopolitan Hotel on Allen Street at about 6:00 A.M. the morning of July 30. King asked for some cartridges for his pistol, saying that someone had attempted to rob him.

King then left the Cosmopolitan and went up the street to the Headquarters Saloon. Thomas Wilson was in the back. Wilson shot at King through a crack in the door - and missed!

Witnesses saw King rolling around in Allen Street with bullets kicking up dirt all around him. They claimed that as many as six shots were fired. Then King got up and went into the Headquarters Saloon. After a short while another shot was heard.

Tom Wilson staggered out the back door of the saloon and to a home about 80 yards away on Fourth Street. He was carried back to the Headquarters Saloon where he died in a short while. The body had one wound - a bullet hole above the left nipple.

A coroners jury ruled: "Wilson came to his death by a leaden bullet shot from a Colt pistol by one King, at the City of Tombstone, County of Pima, Territory of Arizona." Justice Reilly ordered King held for grand jury, and he was taken to Tucson, the county seat.

The grand jury failed to indict King in September. The Epitaph said it was because of the upcoming election in which King wielded considerable political influence.

Strange things happened in 1880 Tombstone and still do. Henry Malcom, age 52, made an attempt to stop a fight between two men. One of them turned to Malcom and said, "Do you want any of this pie?" Then shot him dead. Strangely, the Pima County grand jury let the killer go free, though they did label Malcom a "good Samaritan."

The Earps had money while they were in Tombstone. All of them had jobs; Virgil oft-times had two. On August 27, 1880, they leased the Comstock and the Grasshopper mining claims to R.F. Pixley for $6,000, which was a tidy sum in 1880.

Gravestone - John H. Behan

REWARD!!

A reward of $25 will be paid for the arrest, trial and conviction of each of the thieves who stole six (6) Government mules from Camp John A. Rucker, A. T., on the night of July 21st, 1880.

It is believed these mules were stolen by parties known by the following names:

PONY DIEHL,
A. T. HANSBROUGH,
MAC DEMASTERS.

It is known that the thieves were aided in the secretion of the stolen animals by parties known by the names of

FRANK PATTERSON,
FRANK M'LOWRY,
JIM JOHNSON,

And other parties unknown. It is known that the stolen animals were secreted at or in the vicinity of the McLowry Brothers' ranch, on the Babacomari river, on July 25th, 1880; and it is also believed that they were there branded on the left shoulder over the Government brand, U. S., by the letter and figure D 8.

Evidence to assist in the conviction of the thieves will be furnished by the undersigned.

An additional reward of $25 will be paid for the recovery and delivery of each of these stolen animals to the undersigned.

J. H. HURST,
First Lieutenant, 12th Infantry, A. A. Q. M., Camp John A. Rucker, A. T.
Charleston, A. T., July 27, 1880.

Chapter III

LEADEN MUSIC

Dick Clark, who was a high roller in the gambling circuit all over the West, heard the call of the new boomtown with the strange name, "Tombstone." Little did he know that he would spend the rest of his life there. Clark arrived early in the year 1880. By the time that Milt Joyce had his Oriental Saloon ready to open in July, 1880, Clark and his two partners had already made an arrangement to lease the gambling rooms in the saloon.

His two partners were Bill Harris, who had held interests in the Long Branch Saloon in Dodge City; and Lou Rickabaugh, another gambler who was well-known all through the West. Between the lavish surroundings (built by Joyce) and the attractive gambling layout, provided by the trio (Rickabaugh - Clark - Harris) much of the gambling business in Tombstone was diverted to the Oriental.

Other local gamblers took notice of this decline in their business. Several of them led by a would-be thug and a gunman named Johnny Tyler, began to cause trouble in the Oriental every night. Tyler reasoned that if he and his rowdy friends kept the Oriental in such a tumultuous state all the time that the owners were continually dealing with these problems, they would soon give in and perhaps, offer him a percentage of their gambling layout. The least that could happen with such a program was that the gambling customers would go elsewhere: back to their old haunts (or so Tyler thought).

Lou Rickabaugh had other ideas, however. Even though

Milt Joyce

Owner of the Oriental Saloon

(Photo courtesy of Harry Stewart)

Tyler and his friends were quite successful in creating chaos and driving good customers away, Lou, the major owner in the gambling concession, refused to do business with Tyler, although it appeared that if he didn't take some sort of action, he might lose everything.

In order to get rid of Tyler and his ruffians, Rickabaugh sold Wyatt Earp an interest in the Oriental gambling concession (not in the saloon itself).

Wyatt's first act was to throw Tyler bodily out of the Oriental. While Wyatt was busily occupied with this chore, Doc Holliday stood quietly, hand on his pistol, smiling at Tyler's friends, who were most anxious to help him, but not anxious enough to go against Holliday.

Tyler went down the street, found himself a pistol and came back to the Oriental. Livid with anger at how he had been publicly humiliated, he barged right into the saloon and invited Doc out into the street. Doc pushed right up to his face and challenged him to fight where they stood. It was obvious to everyone present that Tyler was deathly afraid of Doc. Finally, he turned and ran through the front doors.

Doc smiled and remarked "Still running." From that time on, every time Johnny Tyler appeared anywhere in town, someone would call out, "Still running, Johnny?" and everyone present would burst out laughing. Tyler was literally laughed out of Tombstone. However, Doc made a very bitter enemy, as he would find out a few years later.

On October 12, 1880, a strange article appeared in two of the local papers.

The Daily Epitaph carried the following:

"Leaden Music"

"About 12:30 on Sunday night last a shooting affray took place at the Oriental Saloon, corner First (Fifth) and Allen, between M.E. Joyce, one of the proprietors, and a man, named Doc Holliday, during the course of which Joyce was shot in the right hand and his partner, Mr. Parker, received a stray bullet in the big toe. The particu-

lars, as we gather them from an eye-witness, are about as follows: During the early evening Holliday had an altercation with Johnny Tyler which boded a shooting scrape. Shortly, before the shooting referred to occurred, Holliday and Joyce came into the Oriental. Joyce went to Tyler and told him to leave the saloon, as he didn't want trouble. Tyler complied and Joyce then made the same request to Holliday. Holliday demurred, and Joyce and he got into an altercation, during which Joyce put Holliday out of the saloon. Holliday, shortly afterward, returned, and as Joyce was coming out from behind the bar, opened fire on him with a self cocker, firing two shots in quick succession. The first shot struck Joyce in the pistol hand, disabling it, the second missed him and passing through the bar, struck Parker on the foot. Joyce kept advancing all the time, and it is said, fired one shot. Closing with Holliday, he struck him on the head with his six-shooter and finally threw him on the floor. While the men were struggling, Officer Bennett appeared upon the scene and separated the combatants, taking Joyce out of the saloon. Holliday was picked up and placed in a chair, it being generally thought, from his bloody appearance, that he was severely, if not fatally, hurt. Such, however, proved not to be the case, and he was arrested by Deputy Marshall Wyatt Earp. A warrant was subsequently issued for his arrest, on the charge of assault with a deadly weapon, with intent to kill. His bail was fixed by Judge Reilly at $200, which we understood, he furnished. Joyce and Parker are both getting along nicely."

The Daily Nugget carried this story:

"SHOOTING AFFRAY"

"Sunday night a dispute arose in the Oriental Saloon between John Tyler and Doc Holliday, two well-known sports, and a scene of bloodshed was imminent. Mutual friends, however, separated and disarmed both, and Tyler went away. Holliday remained at the saloon. M. E. Joyce, one of the proprietors, remonstrated with Holliday about creating a disturbance in the saloon and the conversation resulted in Holliday being bodily fired out by Joyce. The former came in and demanded his pistol from behind the bar, where it had been placed by the officer, who disarmed him. It was not given him and he went out... but in a short time returned and walked toward

Joyce, who was just coming from behind the bar, and with a remark that wouldn't look well in print, turned loose with a self-cocker. Joyce was not more than ten feet away and jumped for his assailant and struck him over the head with a six-shooter, felling him to the floor and lighting on top of him. Officers, White and Bennett were near at hand and separated them, taking the pistols from each. Just how many shots were fired none present seemed able to tell but in casting up accounts Joyce was found to be short through the hand, his partner, Mr. Parker, who was behind the bar, shot through the big toe of the left foot, and Holliday with a blow of the pistol in Joyce's hands. Gus Williams, barkeeper, was accused of firing a shot in the melee but on appearance in court yesterday morning no complainant appeared against him and the charge was dismissed. All the parties directly implicated are still in bed and no direct arrests have been made, although a complaint has been entered against Holliday and he will be brought before Justice Reilly as soon as he is able to appear, probably today."

"On October 12, 1880, Holliday appeared in court in the custody of the town marshal, Fred White. None of the prosecution witnesses appeared in court. The defendant offered a plea of guilty to assault and battery. It was accepted and the charge of assault with a deadly weapon was dismissed. Holliday was fined $20 and costs of $11.25."

The Tombstone Epitaph carried the recovery of Milt Joyce to its final conclusion on October 16, 1880:

"PERSONAL"

"M.E. Joyce is rapidly recovering from his recent wound."

and on October 17, 1880

"ABOUT TOWN"

"M.E. Joyce is now considered out of danger, and will not lose the use of his hand, which was at one time feared."

Again in the Epitaph, on October 23, 1880:

"IMPROVING"

"During the past day or two inflammation set in on M.E. Joyce's wounded hand and at one time it looked as though amputation would have to be resorted to in order to save life. Yesterday, however, showed a change for the better, and chances of saving the hand are much improved."

And on October 24, 1880:

"ABOUT TOWN"

"M.E. Joyce is reported still improving."

Joyce had always been a crony of John Behan's and quite outspoken in his dislike of Doc Holliday and the Earp brothers. Such feelings became more pronounced after Doc had shot up the Oriental. Therefore, when the lease on the gambling concession ended with the year 1881, Joyce told Rickabaugh, his partner and Wyatt Earp to vacate his premises. No one in Tombstone was surprised to discover that John Behan had replaced them.

Reports filtered back to Wyatt and Dick Clark that Behan did not have much money backing - probably only five thousand dollars. The two men went in one night and seated themselves at a faro table. The dealer was a man named Freis (likely the same Freis later named in March of 1882 as one of Morgan Earp's killers).

Wyatt bought one thousand dollars in chips and began to "buck the tiger." Other players gathered around to watch. Wyatt won steadily, and when he knew he had won all Behan's capital, he cashed in. Even though Behan had insisted that he was good for any amount that Wyatt might win, Wyatt refused and insisted on cash for his chips. Finally, Behan rounded up enough money to pay for the chips and counted it out to Wyatt. Deliberately, Wyatt turned and counted out half of it to Dick Clark.

The result was that Behan had to close down the gambling

concession until he could raise more money. Somehow, he was never able to get it to a paying proposition again. He always blamed Wyatt and Holliday for his failure.

Joyce's partner's full name was William Crownover Parker.

ORIENTAL SALOON

Built in 1880 by Milt Joyce was a hangout for the high class gamblers and gunmen. The Earps had a gambling interest here.

It was probably the most elegant salon between Chicago and San Francisco. When it opened the Epitaph wrote: 'twenty burners suspended in chandeliers afford illumination of brilliance and the bright rays reflected from the many colored crystals on the bar which is beautifully carved, furnished in the style of a grand clubroom, with conveniences for the dealers in polished ivory. Milt Joyce displays an exquisite taste in the selection of the furniture and fixtures in his establishment."

Charlie Storms was shot here in 1881. (Luke Short)

"One-Arm" Kelly was shot here in 1881. (McAllister)

William Claibourne was shot here in 1882. (Frank Leslie)

William Kinsman was shot here in 1883. (May Woodman)

In the Justice's Court of *Precinct no 17* Township.

of the *Village* of *Tombstone* County of *Pima A.T.*

The Territory of Arizona

vs.   Plaintiff

J.H. Holliday   Defendant

Action — *Charge assault with a deadly weapon*

Demand $ —

Attorney for Plaintiff

Attorney for Defendant

DATE	PROCEEDINGS

1880
Oct. 11th — On this day M.E. Joice appeared in Court and on oath accused J.H. Holliday of an assault with a deadly weapon with intent to kill. Warrant issued to Fred White Village marshall.

12 — On this day defendant came into Court in custody of the marshall. Subpoened issue for M.E. Joice, J.H. Behan, Woods, Fuller. And the prosecuting witness failing to appear defendant offered a plea of guilty of assault and Battery which was accepted and the charge of assault with a deadly weapon dismissed. And on the said plea of Guilty the justice took two hours to his sentence. And adjourned till 1. o. c.P.m at one o.P.m defendant in court. The said defendant J.H. Holliday is sentenced to pay a fine of twenty dollars and costs. Costs taxed at sheros $halls fees $6.30 Justices fees $5.00) $11.30 or in default thereof to be confined in the county jail of Pima county one day for each dollar of such fine unpaid. Fine paid. line county $21 —

James Reilly
J.P.

52

Chapter IV

TOWN LOT MAKES A MOVE

When Curly Bill Brocius arrived in Tombstone, it was already a wild and woolly boomtown. Allen Street had already become the "most wicked street in the west," and was a constant riot of bedlam and noise, filled with hundreds of new arrivals.

Brocius was described as heavy set, dark skinned, with black eyes, and curly black hair. Crafty as a lobo wolf, he was strong, agile, and unrestricted by any conscience whatever.

On the night of October 27, 1880, six-guns roared without pause up and down Allen Street. Firing their weapons recklessly in any and all directions, the gunmen who led this violence were Curly Bill, Tom and Frank McLaury, Ike and Billy Clanton, Pony Deal, Dick Lloyd, James Johnson, and Jerry Ackerson. The Clanton gang had "treed" Tombstone.

Fred White, 32 years old, had been elected Tombstone's first town marshal on January 4, 1880. The drunken celebration and wild shooting spree had been going on for two days and nights. Marshal White, a fine lawman, knew that he had to make an example of one of the troublemakers, and then disarm the bunch of them. (The ordinance prohibiting the carrying of guns in town had not yet been passed.)

He encountered Curly Bill on the lot where the Bird Cage Theatre now stands. When White ordered Brocius to surrender his weapon, he presented the weapon to the lawman barrel first. White grasped the barrel and a tongue of flame stabbed through the night followed by the dull roar of a .45. White fell, shot through the abdomen, writhing in agony.

Curly Bill had just pulled the trigger on the first shot fired to begin the Earp-Cowboy feud. Echoes of that shot had not diminished before Deputy Sheriff Wyatt Earp laid a gun barrel over Curly Bill's head, knocking him cold. Wyatt then placed Bill under arrest. Brocius never forgave Wyatt Earp for that brutal and humiliating pistol whipping.

Within moments, Morgan Earp and Fred Dodge appeared on the scene. The Tombstone Epitaph, October 28, 1880, carried the story of White's shooting:

> *"About 12:30 last night a series of pistol shots startled the late goers on the streets, and visions of funerals, etc. flitted through the brain of the Epitaph local and the result proved that his surmises were correct. The result in a few words is as follows: A lot of Texas cowboys, as they were called, began firing at the moon and stars on Allen Street, near Sixth, City Marshal White, who happened to be in the immediate neighborhood, interfered to prevent violation of the city ordinance, and was ruthlessly shot by one of the number. Deputy Sheriff Earp, who is ever to the front when duty calls, arrived just in the nick of time. Seeing the Marshal fall he promptly knocked his assailant down with a six-shooter, and as promptly locked him up; and with the assistance of his brothers, Virgil and Morgan, went in pursuit of the others. That he found them an inventory of the roster of the city prison this morning will testify. Marshal White was shot in the left groin, the ball passing nearly through, and being cut from the buttocks, by Dr. Matthews. The wound is a serious though not fatal one. Too much praise cannot be given the Marshal for his gallant attempt to arrest the violators of the ordinance, nor to Deputy Sheriff Earp and his brothers for the energy displayed in bringing the murderers to arrest. At last accounts, 8:00 a.m., Marshal White was sleeping and strong hopes of his ultimate recovery were expected."*

If the times set forth in the newspaper report are accurate, then White was shot about half an hour past midnight, thereby making the date that he was shot October 28, 1880, rather than October 27, 1880.

The Tombstone Epitaph, October 29, 1880, said:

"The party who shot Marshal White Tuesday night was brought before Judge Gray yesterday morning on a warrant charging him with assault to murder. The complaint was made by Deputy Sheriff Earp. The prisoner asked until 10 o'clock to secure counsel. At 10 o'clock the prisoner reappeared in company with his counsel, Judge Haynes of Tucson, and waiving examination, was committed to jail to await the next meeting of the Grand Jury. He gave the name of William Rosciotis and claiming to hail from San Simon County. Rumor at the time being rife that Marshal White would not live until sundown, and that a Vigilance committee was organizing to hang the prisoner; it was deemed best to take him to Tucson. A buggy was at hand and Deputy Sheriff Earp, accompanied by George Collins started. They were guarded for several miles out of town by Messrs. Virgil and Morgan Earp and others."

Fred Dodge (Wells Fargo) added some information to the incident. He said that White was shot near a cabin that was located where the back section of the Bird Cage Theatre is now. Dodge said that when he reached Wyatt, he found him squatting on his heels alongside Curly Bill and Fred White. Curly Bill's friends were shooting at him and the bullets were hitting the cabin and the rock chimney. As Dodge joined him, Wyatt said, "PUT OUT THE FIRE IN FRED'S CLOTHES!" He had been shot at such close range that his clothes were smoldering.

Dodge and Morgan Earp guarded Curly Bill in jail while Wyatt, Virgil, and Doc Holliday went to arrest the others who had been involved. It did not take them long to bring most of them in. By that time the streets were empty, but the jail was filled to overflowing by daybreak. (IT IS SIGNIFICANT TO NOTE THAT IKE CLANTON WAS NOT TO BE FOUND, BUT HAD DISAPPEARED.)

Fred White died on Saturday, October 30, 1880. However, he did say before his death that Curly Bill was not responsible.

The gun had discharged because he had tried to pull it away from its owner. The poor man probably died thinking he had been killed in an accident.

The editor of the Epitaph printed some very caustic remarks on the sermon rendered at Marshal White's funeral.

The November 1, 1880 edition read:

> *"The circumstances attending the death of Fred White, Marshal of Tombstone, who was murdered in the discharge of his duty, called out the largest assemblage which has ever followed to the tomb any deceased person in Tombstone. The funeral services were held in Gird's Hall and long ere the hour for the funeral services the spacious building was crowded to its utmost capacity. Reverent McIntyre preached the funeral sermon, and took occasion to indulge in a speculative philosophy of the great unknown, of which he is as ignorant as the babe unborn. To say that the reverend gentleman trenched upon the bounds of common sense is but to echo the sentiments of the vast congregation which had assembled to listen to a funeral sermon and not to hear a dissertation on speculation, would be but stating the exact truth. The reverent knows just as much about the Great Unknown as any living creature who has never been there, and his captious flings at the firemen's resolutions were as injudicious as they were ill-timed. The cortege following the murdered Marshal to the grave was the largest ever seen in our embryo city. It embraced all classes and conditions of society from the millionaire to the mudsill and numbered fully 1,000 persons."*

Mayor Alder Randall appointed Virgil Earp as marshal to replace Fred White on October 28, 1880. The Townlot people (CLARK AND GRAY) gained absolutely nothing from White's death. It is certain that the conspiracy that appointed Fred White as the City Marshal expected him to uphold the views and actions of Clark, Gray and Company and not those of the business people. They were doomed to disappointment - as White, a man of integrity, stoutly defended the people who were on the lots, and he maintained their interests until the courts could decide the issue. Virgil Earp not only took over White's job, but assumed his stand in protecting the business people from Clark & Gray.

Curly Bill had an arraignment before Judge Gray in Tombstone. He was advised of the charges, then bail was set. (REMEMBER THAT GRAY IS THE TOWN LOT COMPANY.)

The gunman had a preliminary hearing in Tucson, the county seat, before Justice of the Peace Neugass on December 27, 1880. That worthy, after hearing all the evidence and testimony, ruled that there was not sufficient evidence to hold Brocius for trial and released him from custody.

Curly Bill was released mainly because Marshal White had stated that his wounding had been an accident; a gunsmith, Jacob Gruber, testified that Curly Bill's gun was defective and could be fired at half-cock and Wyatt Earp also testified in his behalf. This was a political move on Wyatt's part. It was his way of making sure that Bob Paul became Sheriff of Pima County. It is difficult to believe that Fred White was shot accidentally. It is known that the Town Lot Gang hated White because he continually interrupted their operations and protected the "Squatters." Curly Bill was on the street with a number of Cowboys who were shooting holes in the sky, yet he wasn't shooting with them. What was he waiting for? White? When White arrested him his pistol was loaded with six rounds, which is contrary to all safety measures in the West. Why? Because he expected to have to shoot his way out of town after killing White. He didn't expect Wyatt to show up so soon and pistol whip him. Was he a hired gun, hired by the Town Lot people? You bet he was. He and his men had been their hirelings since the beginning.

Curly Bill and the Cowboys had two places they really liked - Galeyville on the eastern slopes of the Chiricahua Mountains and Charleston on the San Pedro River. Charleston, a mill town, had about 800 residents and the only law was "Justice Jim" Burnett. Jim ran his legal office strictly for personal profit and seldom concerned himself with the Cowboys. If they didn't get in his way he was happy to ignore them.

Galeyville 1882

(John Billingsley photo)

Charleston About 1938

Charleston had no church or regular minister. One Sunday, Reverend John Addison came down to hold religious services in the school house. Ike Clanton, Curly Bill, and a few of their followers decided that they were in dire need of religion and showed up for the service. The moment that these badmen appeared most of the congregation decided that they had urgent business elsewhere.

The sky pilot had courage and continued with his sermon, omitting no detail of the awesome punishment that was reserved in Hell for thieves and murderers. At the end of the sermon, Brocius demanded a hymn. It was so enjoyed by the Cowboys that they kept the reverend singing for over an hour. To show their appreciation they filled the collection plate to overflowing then solemnly and quietly departed.

Reverend Addision never returned to Charleston again.

The following morning Brocius sat "sleeping the sleep of the innocent" in an easy chair on the front porch of Tarbell's Eagle Hotel, when a double barreled shotgun nudged him in the ear. That most impressive weapon was wielded by none other than "Justice Jim," the total law enforcement agency of Charleston.

Cocking both barrels of his formidable weapon, the justice loudly declared his court "in session." Without any waste of the court's time he found the defendant guilty of unlawfully inter- rupting religious services as charged, and levied a fine of $50 on the spot and forced the astounded outlaw to pay up. Brocius loved to tell the story about the time a "court of law" tried him and gave him what he deserved. Then, he would laugh uproariously.

Galeyville, the other outlaw hangout, had begun as a silver camp up in Turkey Creek Canyon. The vein of silver pinched out after a year or so and the town became a ghost town by the end of 1882, inhabited by outlaws for the most part.

San Simon, a tiny railroad stop, lay some 20 miles north of Galeyville. Its total population numbered 35 people, including men, women, children and 10 railroad section hands that were

Chinese.

Robert H. "Bob" Paul, running against Charlie Shibell for the office of Pima County Sheriff made it a red hot election. The sheriff's job was a lucrative plum. Not only did the sheriff's office enforce the law and serve legal papers, it assessed and collected county taxes, keeping a portion for its trouble.

The outlaws did not want Bob Paul as sheriff as he had made things very uncomfortable for them as an employee of Wells Fargo. Worse yet, he was a friend of the Earps.

When the voting was completed on November 2, 1880, and the ballot counting had been completed, the results were that Shibell had won by 58 votes. As a matter of course, Wyatt and Bob Paul checked the ballots from each and every precinct. Each time they were dawn back to Precinct 27, which was San Simon. It was extremely difficult to believe that this tiny precinct had been able to muster 104 total votes and that they tallied 103 for Shibell and 1 for Paul!

Wyatt resigned as a Pima County deputy sheriff on November 9, 1880. His intention was to assist Bob Paul in his legal contest of the election. Their suspicions became much stronger when it was discovered that the election polling location had first been placed at the home of Joe Hill (Cowboy and close friend of John Ringo). Paul supporters became even more suspicious when they heard that the election inspector was Ike Clanton and the election judges were A.H. Thompson and John Ringo. The man who had certified Precinct 27 votes was Henry Johnson. No one could determine who this Henry Johnson was. Even the county supervisors could not explain who he was.

If the court decided that the San Simon Precinct votes were illegal, then Bob Paul would become sheriff, as Shibell's vote total would be reduced by 103.

The election had not been held at Joe Hill's house as planned, but at the house of John Magill. James Johnson was finally identified as the mysterious Henry Johnson, who had certified the precinct votes. Wyatt Earp discovered that he was the James K. Johnson who was shooting up Allen Street the night Marshal White was killed. Moreover, he was the Johnson that testified at Curly Bill's preliminary hearing. He was also a member of Curly Bill's gang of rustlers.

Bob Paul started his legal suit to contest the election on November 19, 1880. Eventually, the case was transferred to Tucson's district court and the trial began on January 17, 1881. The Arizona Star printed on January 20, 1881: "There has been some big cheating somewhere, and by some persons. It was clear that there had been reckless counting at Tombstone, fraud at San Simon and a careless election board at Tres Alamos."

When James Johnson testified in court, he admitted that he had voted as George Johnson. He admitted to a number of other startling facts, too. Such as: Less than 15 people showed up at the polling booth on voting day: that only 3 or 4 votes cast were legal: that new polling lists were made up so that 103 voters for Shibell could be included: and that Phin Clanton had taken possession of the ballots. He said that the Cowboys had intended to have the election at Ike Clanton's house, but they could not determine whether his house was in New Mexico or Arizona.

When John Magill testified that his house had been the polling spot, he also swore that he had voted in the election but had never registered. In fact, he had no idea of what registration was.

R.B. Kelly swore that he had registered in Willcox, but that the election judges (Ringo and Thompson) let him vote in Galeyville. Kelly was also designated as a poll watcher but later admitted that in the San Simon Precinct, more votes were cast than there were voters.

Tombstone had to be in on anything that was dishonest. A recount of the votes was made and this time Paul had 402 votes and Shilbell had 354. Sixty-two were kept from a closer examination.

When this was done, it revealed that of the total 62 votes, 42 had been cast for Paul, but his name had been erased and Shibell's written in. Ike Clanton was supposed to testify, but did not. Papers for his subpoena had been issued to John Behan, but Behan did not serve them. Later, Ike told Behan that "he had armed his people and was not going to Tucson to court!" He didn't!

Deputy Bill Oury, a friend of both Clanton and Behan, was also issued papers to subpoena Ike, but Oury never served them. Under oath, he admitted that he had been given the subpoena and that he had not served it. When asked why not, he yelled, "That's my business!" And it must have been true as he was never called to account.

The opinion of Judge French was filed on January 29, 1881. It destroyed the Cowboy hopes. His decision upheld the court at the Tres Alamos Precinct, reprimanded George Atwood, the election inspector for not exercising more control over the Tombstone ballots, and declared Shilbell's 103 votes at San Simon invalid. The final results were, Bob Paul had 1,684 votes and Charley Shibell 1,628. Paul was the duly elected sheriff of Pima County! But all was not over; Shibell immediately filed an appeal to the Arizona Supreme Court. That appeal allowed Shibell to remain in the sheriff's office until the appeal was decided, which was over two months.

The Supreme Court of Arizona Territory dismissed the appeal on April 12, 1881, legally making Bob Paul the sheriff of Pima County. The Territorial Legislature carved a piece from Pima County's eastern part and created Cochise County effective February 1, 1881. The irony is that the time from the election until the Supreme Court made Bob Paul sheriff took Tombstone out of Pima County jurisdiction.

Wyatt Earp's saddle horse had disappeared and he assumed that someone had stolen it. It was late in 1880 when Sherman McMasters notified Wyatt that he had seen Deputy Sheriff Gates, a friend of the Cowboy faction, ride into a Charleston stable on Wyatt's missing horse. Even then the horse was stabled in Frank Stillwell's stable. Just as Wyatt rode up to the stable, Billy Clanton was riding out - on Wyatt's horse. When Wyatt demanded his horse, Billy began to bluster and argue. But, when he saw Wyatt meant business he dismounted, took his bridle and saddle, then relinquished the horse.

Herman Wellish store in Charleston

Bridge across San Pedro River between Charleston and Millville. Note Millville and Tombstone Mining Company buildings in the background

Tombstones first big fire

Ben Sippy

(Kate Poteet photo)

Born in New York, Elected town Marshal January 4, 1881. Left on a leave of absence and never returned.

Chapter V.

POLITICS, OUTLAWS, AND FIRE

Late in the year 1880, "Old Man" Clanton gave his ranch on the San Pedro to his sons and moved to the Animas Valley in New Mexico, a short distance north of the Mexican border.

At about the same time, the McLaury brothers sold their holdings on the San Pedro and settled on a ranch four miles from Soldiers Hole in the Sulphur Springs Valley.

With these strategic moves the Clantons and their followers had ranches specifically located in the San Pedro Valley, the Sulphur Springs Valley and the Animas Valley; places all near the border and at spots located along the "rustler's trail" that could accept stolen livestock going into or coming out of Mexico, supplying fresh mounts, food, and rest to riders - with no questions asked.

When Wyatt had resigned as Pima County deputy sheriff, Sheriff Charlie Shibell appointed Johnny Behan to fill that vacancy. Now Behan was involved in politics with the county ring, friendly with the Cowboy rustler faction and the Town Lot Company, plus now he represented the county law in Tombstone.

Although the mayor had appointed Virgil to finish Fred White's term, there was a change of plans. On November 12, 1880, a special election was held to fill the town marshal's job for the rest of the year. Ben Sippy beat Virgil in this election, 311 to 259.

Not long after the election Johnny-Behind-the-Deuce

(Michael O'Rourke) shot and killed W.P. Schneider, the Chief Engineer of the Tombstone Mining and Milling Corporation in Charleston on January 14, 1881.

Johnny was arrested and locked in jail. A number of the Cowboy faction were present and they quickly realized that this was an excellent opportunity to cause trouble. They began buying drinks for the already angry miners. When the free whiskey had taken effect they suggested that a lynching party was in order.

George McKelvey, the Charleston constable, saw what the drunk and angry mob were up to and realized that he could not protect his prisoner. He took O'Rourke from jail, put him into a buckboard pulled by a team of mules, and headed for Tombstone with a lynch mob on his heels.

Three miles out of Tombstone McKelvey knew that his mules were finished. His pursuers were beginning to close in as he neared Jack McCann's Last Chance Saloon. A horseman showed up in front of them; it was Virgil Earp riding Wyatt's race horse, Dick Naylor. McKelvey shouted that he had a prisoner and that a lynch mob was on his tail. Virgil rode in close and took O'Rourke behind him.

O'Rourke was taken to Vogan's Bowling Alley. Jim Earp was tending bar. Wyatt, Virgil, Fred Dodge, and Ben Sippy stood off the angry miners and Cowboys while Morgan guarded the prisoner.

Still in danger, O'Rourke was moved to the Tucson jail from which he escaped on the night of April 17, 1881. Charged with first degree murder and a fugitive from the law, Johnny-Behind-the-Deuce disappeared forever.

When the new county, called Cochise, was being formed the first of February, 1881, the county offices had to be filled by appointment as the regular election was a year away. Many of the appointments were made to people from Tucson which rankled the people living in Tombstone.

Both Wyatt Earp and John Behan wanted the job of county

sheriff. That job was a much desired position as the sheriff was also the tax collector, and, as such, would receive a percentage of the taxes he collected (over $24,000 in 1882).

Both men had considerable experience as lawmen. Wyatt was a Republican and the Territorial Government and Governor were also, but the Democrats ruled Tombstone and Behan was a Democrat. Behan was a big, accomplished politician - Wyatt was not. Still, Behan had some doubts that he would get the appointment, so he approached Wyatt with a deal ... and such a deal.

Behan proposed that Wyatt withdraw and leave the field open for him to be appointed sheriff. In return he would make Wyatt his under-sheriff, and at the regular election next year he would withdraw and let Wyatt run for sheriff unopposed.

The two men made the agreement that Behan had proposed and he became the first sheriff of Cochise County on February 1, 1881. However, once he had secured the appointment, Behan reneged on his agreement with Wyatt and appointed Harry Woods, a Democrat, as his under-sheriff.

William H. Harris, formerly a co-owner of the Long Branch Saloon in Dodge City and now a partner in the Oriental Saloon, sent for two gamblers: Luke Short and Bat Masterson. They arrived in Tombstone around the middle of February, 1881.

Luke Short

Arrived in Tomstone early in 1881. Employed as a dealer in the Oriental Saloon. Killed Charlie Storms on February 25, 1881. Died of dropsy in Geuda Springs, Kansas in 1893.

Short had been in town only a short while when he had an altercation with Charlie Storms on February 25, 1881. Storms was also a gambler. Both men had earned reputations as first class gunmen in some of the toughest boomtowns in the West.

One morning Storms appeared at the Oriental drunk, waving a pistol about. After a brief argument Storms called Short out into the street, telling him he was going to kill him.

Bat Masterson arrived just in time to keep Luke Short from killing Charlie Storms. He stepped between them and asked Short not to shoot. Then he took Storms to his hotel room and calmed him down. Masterson then went back to the Oriental to talk to Short. He considered both men his friend. When he arrived back at the saloon, Short was outside, standing before the front entrance to the Oriental. As he was explaining that Storms was just drunk Storms suddenly appeared. He took Short's arm and pulled him off the sidewalk, pulling his pistol at the same time. Luke was too fast for him, however, and pulled his own gun, put it against Storms and shot him through the heart.

Parsons said that even though he was shot through the heart that Storms fired his single action pistol four times (inaccurately). Short, apparently unconcerned, went back to his game in the Oriental.

Charlie Storms was taken to his eternal rest in Boothill.

Hardly had the new county been formed and the Territorial Governor was already worried about the lawless conditions. Governor John C. Fremont called attention to these lawless conditions in southeastern Arizona in his speech to the Eleventh Territorial Legislature on February 21, 1881:

> *"I have to ask the earnest attention of the council to the conditions of southeastern Arizona and the Mexican border, which requires immediate action from the executive authority of the territory. It is well known to the Legislative Assembly that life and property on both sides of the line are insecure, and to prevent the rapid increase of this insecurity and danger, decided measures must be*

*adopted to break up and destroy the organized bands of
outlaws which now infest the region, to the great danger
and detriment of our citizens and to the manifest risk of
serious complications with the government of the United
States."*

The shooting of Marshal Fred White by Curly Bill, near
Midnight on October 27, 1880, was the opening incident of
the war between the Cowboys, the Earps and Holliday. Many
more incidents were soon to follow.

On March 15, 1881, the Kinnear & Company stage (running from Tombstone to Benson) was traveling near
Contention City when a hold-up was attempted.

As the stage had slowed going up a small incline about two
hundred yards from Drew's Station and about a mile the other
side of Contention City, a man stepped into the road from the
east side and called out, "Hold!"

At the same time eight men made their appearance and a
shot was fired, followed quickly by another. One of the shots
stuck Budd Philpot, the driver, who fell between the wheelers,
still holding onto the reins. Frightened, the coach horses broke
into a dead run. Bob Paul, Well's Fargo & Company's messenger, traded shots with the stage's attackers and, at the same
time, tried to gain control of the run-away horses.

The stage had traveled about a mile before the horses could
be brought under control. At that time, it was discovered that
there had been another casualty. One of the shots had fatally
wounded Pete Roering, a passenger from Kenosha, Wisconsin.

Paul took the stage and passengers on into Benson, then
started back to the scene of the murders. Meanwhile, the
sounds of the shots and the runaway coach brought several
men from Drew's Station to the scene of the tragedy. They
found Philpot lying dead in the road. A messenger informed
agent Cowen of the incident and, within a short while, he had
a posse of thirty men on the trail of the killers.

Sheriff Behan, the newly appointed Sheriff of Cochise
County, also rode out with a posse. They soon joined forces

with the Earp posse: Behan, Bob Paul, Wyatt, Virgil and Morgan Earp, with Bat Masterson, all allied to capture the bandits.

At Len Redfield's ranch, Wyatt and Morgan captured one of the killers named Luther King. Paul and Wyatt told King a frightening story: that "Big Nose" Kate had been on the stage and one of the bandit shots had killed her, threatening him with the deadly Doc Holliday. Terrorized, he named Harry Head, Billy Leonard, and Jim Crane as three others who had been involved in the two murders.

Tombstone's Well's Fargo agent, Marshall Williams, and John Behan escorted the prisoner to the Tombstone jail. Supposedly locked in the jail by the sheriff, King went out the back door, while Harry Jones was preparing a bill of sale for the prisoner to sell his horse to John Dunbar. Someone had conveniently left a saddled horse tied just outside. King mounted up and was never seen again. The Nugget claimed that he was allowed to escape because he was an important witness against Doc Holliday.

The killers finally made their escape into the wilds of old Mexico although the Earp posse dogged their trail through Arizona's most hostile country for over three hundred miles.

The four other outlaws involved in the stage holdup were never positively identified. Some of the older residents and some historians believed that they were Ike Clanton, Frank Stilwell, Pete Spencer, and "Curly Bill" Brocius.

(Author's Note: "Budd" Philpot was normally the stage driver and Bob Paul was the shotgun messenger that Well's Fargo sent along. However, on the fateful night of March 15, 1881, Philpot had been having stomach miseries and Paul had been kind enough to switch places with him and give him some relief. Bob Paul had given the outlaws a great deal of aggravation as an employee of Well's Fargo. He was also a good friend of Wyatt Earp's and they could forecast their future with Bob Paul as Sheriff of Pima County working in conjunction with the Earp brothers. Actually, the shooters intended to kill Bob

Paul - but he was in the wrong place at the right time and they murdered the wrong man.)

Later that year, a strange newspaper article appeared. It read:

"A MYSTERY SOLVED"

"One of the parties killed by Mexican regulars in New Mexico was the notorious Jim Crane, the last survivor of the stage robbers who murdered Philpot near Benson last spring. From a party who met Crane a few days before his death, the Tombstone Nugget learns the following additional particulars concerning the attempted stage robbery.

To many it has always seemed a mystery that the parties mentioned should have killed Philpot and spared Bob Paul, Well's Fargo & Company messenger. According to Crane, however, when the ambushed robbers fired at Philpot, they thought it was Paul, as the two had swapped places, Paul acting as driver and poor Budd as messenger. They meant to kill Paul, thinking that his death would result in the stoppage of the stage, and the easy plunder of Well's Fargo & Company's box and the passengers. The change from messenger to driver, so Crane says, was made somewhere between the change station and the place of ambush. This he claimed to know as he was the party detailed to watch for the stage, and signal it to his comrades. Why the change was made will probably never be known until the great judgment. Suffice it that poor Philpot now sleeps peacefully under the daisies, and the intended victim, Paul, still lives, sheriff of Pima County, and a dreaded terror to the class of whom his intended murders formed a part."

The Cowboy faction seized this opportunity to place the blame for the attempted holdup and two murders on Doc Holliday. (After all, Billy Leonard had been identified as one of the killers, and wasn't he a close friend of Holliday from their New Mexico days?)

Doc took a lot of hard words from their accusations, but then his famous temper began to react to such ridiculous charges. The first such example was in the court of A.J.

Wallace.

*"A.J. Wallace, Justice of the Peace, March 1, 1881 -
December 31, 1991.*

April 13, 1881. Territory vs. J.H. Holliday:

Threats against life. Discharged on pymt. of costs."

Another such reaction followed soon after and was noted in
the Tombstone Epitaph, May 30, 1881:

*"Doc Holliday has been indicated by the Grand Jury on
account of participation in a shooting affray some time
since. He was released on bonds."*

Arizona almost lost its head outlaw at large.

*Arizona Weekly Star. Tucson, A.T., Thursday, May 26,
1881.*

"CURLY BILL:

*"THIS NOTED DESPERADO "GETS IT IN THE NECK" AT
GALEYVILLE.*

*The notorious "Curly Bill," the man who murdered
Marshal White at Tombstone last fall, and who has been
concerned in several other desperate and lawless affrays
in Southeastern Arizona, has at last been brought to
grief, and there is likely to be a vacancy in the ranks of
our border desperadoes. The affair occurred at Galeyville
Thursday. A party of eight or nine cowboys, "Curly Bill"
and his partner Jim Wallace among the number, were in
town enjoying themselves in their usual manner, when
Deputy Sheriff Breakenridge, of Tombstone, who was at
Galeyville on business, happened along.*

*Wallace made some insulting remark to the deputy, at
the same time flourishing his revolver in an aggressive
manner. Breakenridge did not pay much attention to this
"break" of Wallace, but quietly turned around and left
the party. Shortly after this "Curly Bill," who, it would
seem, had a friendly feeling for Breakenridge, insisted
that Wallace should go and find him and apologize for
the insult given. This Wallace was induced to do, and
after finding Breakenridge he made the apology, and the
latter accompanied him back to the saloon where the
cowboys were drinking. By this time "Curly Bill," who
had drank just enough to make him quarrelsome, was in*

one of his most dangerous moods, and evidently desirous of increasing his record as a man-killer. He commenced to abuse Wallace, who, by the way, has some pretensions himself as a desperado and "bad man" generally, and finally said, "You d---d Lincoln county s—of a b----, I'll kill you anyhow." Wallace immediately went outside the door of the saloon, "Curly Bill" following close behind him. Just as the latter stepped outside, Wallace, who had meanwhile drawn his revolver, fired, the ball penetrating the left side of "Curly Bill's" neck and passing through came out the right cheek, not breaking the jaw-bone. A scene of the wildest excitement ensued in the town. The other members of the cowboy party surrounded Wallace and threats of lynching him were made by them. The law-abiding citizens were in doubt of what course to pursue. They did not wish any more bloodshed, but were in favor of allowing the lawless element to "have it out" among themselves. But Deputy Sheriff Breakenridge decided to arrest Wallace, which he succeeded in doing without meeting any resistance. The prisoner was taken before Justice Ellenwood, and after examination into the facts of the shooting he was discharged.

The wounded and apparently dying desperado was taken into an adjoining building, and a doctor summoned to dress his wounds. After examining the course of the bullet, the doctor pronounced the wound dangerous, but not necessarily fatal, the chances for and against recovery being about equal. Wallace and "Curly Bill" have been partners and fast friends for the past five or six months, and so far as is known, there was no cause for the quarrel, it being simply a drunken brawl. A great many people in southeastern Arizona will regret that the termination was not fatal to one or both of the participants. Although the wound is considered very dangerous, congratulations at being freed from this dangerous character are now rather premature, as men of his class usually have a wonderful tenacity of life."

Ben Sippy requested and received from the City Council a two week leave of absence. He left town on June 6, 1881. The council appointed Virgil "acting marshal" during his absence.

Virgil's first major problem after his reinstatement was when Denny McCann slapped Ike Clanton outside the Wells Fargo office. Both men drew guns, but Virgil prevented any gunplay. The Daily Epitaph remarked that Marshal Earp prevented one funeral, perhaps two.

After awhile it became apparent that Sippy had no intentions of returning to his job. It became known later that he had been heavily in debt, had been reprimanded by the council for leaving town without permission or notification, and for releasing prisoners without authorization. This coupled with the fact that the job was quite demanding plus he was unable to cope with all the warring factions in town made him want out.

On June 28, 1881, three weeks after Ben Sippy had departed, the major and city council made Virgil the permanent Chief of Police, Marshal, Health Inspector, and Fire Marshal, with the salary of $100 a month. His office was located upstairs over the Crystal Palace.

Tombstone has always had a fear of fire. The desert climate sears everything until it is totally dry. Therefore, fire spreads most rapidly, sweeping through anything and everything it touches.

Strangely enough, Tombstone's first big fire was caused by its citizens favorite drink - whiskey! A single barrel of whiskey exploded and caught fire and in three hours four blocks of business buildings were totally destroyed.

On June 22, 1881, Messrs. Alexander & Thompson, proprietors of the Arcade Saloon, three doors east of the Oriental Saloon, had a barrel of liquor that had been condemned for quite some time. They decided that it was a good time to return it.

They rolled it out in front of the bar and knocked the bung out. A measurement of the liquor still in the barrel was needed. The bartender was called out to help. Unfortunately, he had a lighted cigar in his mouth. It caught the escaping gas on fire and it spread into the barrel which exploded, throwing flaming liquor in all directions.

L.L. Sales and David Cotter were also in the saloon. Sales later reported that the concussion was horrendous and that the entire front of the saloon was in flame instantly. The front entrance was blocked by flames, but the two men and the bartender managed to get out the back door. In less than three minutes the flames had spread to the buildings on either side.

When the fire broke through the front entrance, the alarm was given and many people rushed to the scene. But, before anything could be done, the store of Meyers Brothers, Glover & Co., and the Oriental had all burst into flame.

It was apparent that not much could be done about the buildings, so many started to save money, books, and other valuables. Milton B. Clapp, manager of Safford, Hudson & Co.'s bank put all the money and valuables into the inner safe then fled out the back with the books as the ceiling began falling in around his head. (this is now the site of Marie's.)

Milt Joyce, who owned the Oriental Saloon, ran to his safe and was trying to unlock it when the flames reached him. He was forced to flee for his life, leaving $1,200 in green backs and a large amount of deposits. Joyce lost it all.

Wells Spicer, whose office was on Fifth Street, saved his official and private papers, then ordered that the frame building be demolished to stop the spread of the fire. The fire reached it before its destruction could be accomplished. The firemen made Herculean efforts to stem the fire - but it swept on to Fremont Street and burned across Allen Street to Toughnut, reaching as far as Seventh Street. It was stopped here because of several empty lots. The north side of Fremont buildings were saved by wet blankets and copious amounts of water.

By 6:00 P.M. only charred skeletons of buildings still stood, smoke still rising from them. The flames were slowing dying out.

A total of 66 stores, saloons, restaurants, and business places were destroyed. The loss was set at $175,000 of which only $25,000 was covered by insurance. Rebuilding was rapidly accomplished.

"Big Nose" Kate and Doc Holliday lived together for a time in Tombstone, but Doc had gone back to his drinking and gambling and Kate to her operations as a sometime prostitute. They spent most of their time together arguing and fighting. Lately, Kate had been showing up drunk and, as their quarreling continued, she became abusive. After awhile, Doc had enough and threw her out.

When Kate was out on a drunken binge berating Doc for throwing her out, Sheriff Behan and county supervisor, Milt Joyce, found her in a deplorable condition. While she aired her troubles with Doc to all who would listen, they bought her all the whiskey she could drink. They sympathized with her and suggested how she might "even the score" with Doc.

Eventually, they persuaded her to sign an affidavit implicating Doc in the attempted hold up and murders of Budd Philpot and Peter Roerig. Justice Wells Spicer issued a warrant for Doc's arrest on the strength of Kate's affidavit.

"COURT PROCEEDINGS"

"U.S. Commissioner Court - Wells Spicer U.S. Court Commissioner.

United States vs. John H. Holliday - For attempt to rob U.S. Mail at the time of killing Budd Philpot; waiting examination."

"Justice Court - Wells Spicer, J.P.

Territory vs. John H. Holliday

On charge of murder of Budd Philpot. Continued to July 6, at 9:00 A.M.

Bonds $5,000."

"IMPORTANT ARREST"

"A warrant was sworn out yesterday before Justice Spicer for the arrest of Doc Holliday, a well known character here, charging him with complicity in the murder of Budd

Philpot, and the attempted stage robbery near Contention some four months ago, and he was arrested by Sheriff Behan. The warrant was issued upon the affidavit of Kate Elder, with whom Holliday had been living for sometime past. Holliday was taken before Justice Spicer in the afternoon, who released him upon bail in the amount of $5,000, Wyatt Earp, J. Meagher, and J.L. Melgren becoming sureties. The examination will take place before Judge Spicer at 9 o'clock this morning."

The case was called for hearing on July 9, 1881:

"Court Proceedings, Justice Court. Spicer: Judge.

The case of Territory vs. John A. (sic) Holliday, was called for hearing yesterday morning at 10 o'clock. The District Attorney, addressing court, said that he had examined all the witnesses summoned for the prosecution and from their statements he was satisfied that there was not the slightest evidence to show the guilt of the defendant; that the statements of the witnesses did not even amount to a suspicion of the guilt of the defendant, and he was therefore asking that the complaint be withdrawn and the case be dismissed.

The court thereupon dismissed the case and discharged the defendant, and thus ended what, at one time, was supposed to be an important case."

When Kate sobered up she realized what she had done, regretted her actions and repudiated her affidavit accusing Doc. She claimed that she had signed a paper while drinking with Behan and Joyce, but she could not remember what it was.

The Nugget reported:

"Miss Kate Elder sought surcease of sorrow in the flowing bowl. She succeeded so well that when she found her name written on the Chief's register with the 'Ds' appended to it. She paid her matriculation fee of $12.50, took her degrees and departed."

John Henry Holiday about 1881

Chapter VI

BORDER WARFARE - one thru five

But, Kate, being the independent spirit she was, could not let it be. She found Doc, blamed him for all her problems, threw a cursing fit, and threatened to kill him. Doc had her arrested to get rid of her.

She was charged with "threats against life" and faced the U.S. Court on a writ of habeas corpus. Kate hired Wells Spicer to defend her. He was the judge who had heard her charges against Doc. She appeared before United States Court Commissioner of the First Judicial District, T.J. Drum, who (for whatever reason) dismissed the writ and discharged the defendant.

By this time, Doc had exhausted his patience with Kate. He put her on a stage for Globe. Kate worked in a hotel there for a time. She did visit Doc in Tombstone on occasion, but only a few days at a visit.

Even though the case against Doc had been thrown out, Wyatt knew that the only way to clear Doc (and the Earp name as well) was to capture one or all the real killers; Crane, Leonard, or Head, and force them to make a full confession as to everyone involved.

Such a capture and confession would serve a two-fold purpose. (One of which would most-likely be catapulting him into the sheriff's office the next election.) Now, all he had to do was find out where the men he wanted were hiding out and go get them - and Wyatt knew the man who would know exactly where they were.

Wyatt located Ike Clanton and made him a proposition. If Ike would lure his outlaw friends to where Wyatt could kill or capture them, he would see that Ike received the three thousand, six hundred dollar reward that Well's Fargo had offered for them. It required several meetings before Ike was convinced. He said that he would need some help in the venture and chose Joe Hill and Frank McLaury. Still cautious, Ike wanted verification from Well's Fargo that the reward would be paid dead or alive.

"SAN FRANCISCO ~ JUNE 7, 1881

MARSHALL WILLIAMS - TOMBSTONE, ARIZONA
YES, WE WILL PAY REWARD FOR
THEM DEAD OR ALIVE.
L.F. ROWELL"

(Author's Note: Rowell was Well's Fargo President, John J. Valentine's assistant in San Francisco.)

All Ike's requirements were met and the location picked for the capture of the killers was designated as the McLaury brother's ranch, which was in the Sulphur Springs Valley, not far from Soldier's Hole. Joe Hill had already gone over into New Mexico to convince the fugitives to come to the McLaury ranch.

Hill had been gone for several days when he returned - with bad news. Leonard and Head had tried to hold up the Haslett brother's store and the Haslett boys had shot them down. This information rattled Ike pretty good but, when he remembered that Marshal Williams had also seen that telegraph from Well's Fargo verifying the dead or alive reward, he went berserk. As he realized what his rustler friends would do to him when they learned that he was willing to sell them out for money, he became petrified with fear.

During July, 1881, one of Curly Bill's men in old Mexico received information that smugglers were bringing a rich mule train up into Arizona. He informed Bill that the route they would take would be through Skeleton Canyon, which twists and turns through some very rough country of the Peloncillo Mountains. The mule train would come through San Luis Pass into the Animas Mountains, across the Animas Valley into San Simon, to the San Pedro Valley and into the Santa Cruz Valley. Outside Tucson, the smugglers would set up camp and invest their silver 'dobe dollars in contraband merchandise to smuggle back into Mexico.

Skeleton Canyon earned its grisly name because of the many murders that occurred there, and bodies left without burial. Vultures and wild animals stripped the flesh leaving the bones scattered about.

On August 1, 1881, the train of smugglers led a line of the small Andalusian mules through the rocky, twisting trails of Skeleton Canyon never realizing that other men, with murder in mind, lay in wait. They were totally unprepared when riflemen hidden in the rocks and brush began to cut them down. The Mexican smugglers had no chance at all. In that narrow canyon of death there was no place to go except up or down the trail. The hidden riflemen commanded the rocky walls on both sides. As the Mexicans fell, the little mules stampeded up the canyon, carrying the bags of 'dobe dollars.

Curly Bill and his killers raced after the mules shooting them to stop them. Mules and men were left lying where they fell in Devil's Kitchen. The killers took their ill-gotten gains to Cave Creek Canyon where they divided $4,000 in Mexican silver bullion and coin, mescal, horses and cattle. It required several days for the outlaws to spend their money on women and whiskey in the saloons of Galeyville and Charleston. A good bit of their loot was won by Johnny Ringo and Joe Hill in poker games.

Later, Ringo told that the Skeleton Canyon ambushers were himself; the Clantons, "Old Man," Ike, and Billy; Frank and

Tom McLaury; Jim Hughes; "Rattlesnake Bill," Joe Hill, Charlie Snow; Jake Gauze; and Charlie Thomas.

Curly Bill had sent a half dozen of his cowboy; Alex Arnett, Jake Gauze, Bud Snow, Jake McKenzie, John McGill, and Milt Hicks, to old Mexico on a cattle rustling operation. These men stole approximately a hundred head of cattle in Sonora. It was a quick strike and they stampeded the animals through San Luis Pass into the Animas Valley. Ringo, Tall Bell, Charlie Thomas, Charlie Greene, Jim Crane, Billy Lang, Joe Hill, John Greene, and Curly Bill rode over from Roofless 'Dobe ranch and joined the men with the stolen herd. They drove the cattle to "Old Man" Clanton's ranch.

The cattle were sold to "Old Man;" he rested them and then headed them to the nearest market: Tombstone, for a quick sale and profit. The journey was not to end in the manner he expected. Six men rode along with him: Dixie Lee Gray, Billy Lang, Bud Snow, Billy Byers, Harry Ernshaw, and Jim Crane. The latter was one of those who had held up the Contention stage, killing Budd Philpot and Pete Roering in the process on March 15, 1881. Warrants were out for his arrest and Wyatt Earp wanted desperately to capture him.

The planned route of travel was from Clanton's ranch through Guadalupe Canyon in the San Bernardino Valley, through the Sulphur Springs Valley around the Dragoon Mountains to Tombstone. They made camp the first night in Guadalupe Canyon about one mile south of the International border, near the area where Arizona, New Mexico, Sonora, and Chihuahua meet.

(Author's Note: Glenn Boyer, the foremost Earp historian, and many natives of that area insist that this was Skeleton Canyon and not Guadalupe. A highly defined map shows that what they say is entirely logical, probably the most logical location. However, the evidence presented here will stress Guadalupe Canyon because newspaper and other accounts of the time label that location.

From this point, many words have been written and a variety of versions have been presented. The author will attempt to relate the information available at the time of the massacre.)

The Tucson Arizona Weekly Citizen, May 22, 1881, tells of a raid made by four cowboys from Cachise (sic) County on a cattle ranch ten miles below the international border. Between four and five hundred head of cattle were stolen. The Mexican owners organized and chased the rustlers, catching them before they reached the border. A gun battle ensued in which three of the cowboys were killed and another seriously wounded. Jose Juan Vasquez offered to take him to his ranch and care for him, but the desperado shot Vasquez through the heart. The other Mexicans emptied their guns into the murderer.

On June 16, 1881, the Arizona Weekly Star printed a follow up article that told of a party of seventy cowboys leaving Willcox for the purpose of making a raid on Fronteras, Sonora to avenge the deaths of the four parties who were killed three weeks ago in that area. They openly avowed to wipe out the town of Fronteras in revenge for the Americans killed.

The paper expected this force of cowboys to encounter Mexican Federal Troops which would provide a warm fight.

"The cowboys are reckless, daring fighters, good shots, ride good horses and don't place a great deal of value on life. Should any damage be done to our Mexican neighbors, the United States will not be able to escape censure. This whole affair was organized on American soil and with an open and avowed purpose of murder, robbery, and outlawry."

Such episodes along the border coupled with the Skeleton Canyon massacre on August 1, 1881, set the stage for the entire border country to explode in gunfire. Explode it did on August 13, 1881, when "Old Man" Clanton and his men were shot down. The Tombstone Daily Epitaph of August 16, 1881, carried a full story:

"MORE BORDER TROUBLES"
"Mexicans on a Raid - five men
killed including the notorious Jim Crane"

"About half past four o'clock last evening news reached town that Dick Gray, youngest son of M. Gray of our city and well known here, had been killed together with four others by Mexicans near the town of Gillespie, New Mexico. The news caused considerable excitement and knots of curious inquirers gathered about the streets eager to hear the particulars. About an hour later Andy Aines and Joe Trebble arrived in town from the scene of the murders and confirmed the news. There are several reports as to the causes that led to this lamentable affair. The immediate particulars are about as follows: A party consisting of Wm. Lang, Dick Gray, Jim Crane, Charlie Snow, the senior Clanton, Wm. Byers, and Harry Ernshaw camped last Friday night in Guadalupe Canyon about one hundred and ten miles east from Tombstone and very near to the Mexican line. Early on Saturday the party was attacked by Mexicans and Lang, Gray, Crane, Snow, and Clanton were killed. Byers escaped with a wound in the abdomen while Ernshaw ran away amidst a shower of bullets, one of which grazed his nose. It is estimated that the Mexican party numbered from 25 to 30 men. The condition of the camp indicated that the attack was made just as the murdered men were about getting up; one had evidently been killed while yet laying down.

Jim Crane, it will be remembered, was involved in the murder of "Budd" Philpot. He joined the fated party, we are informed, at midnight Friday and was only camped with them for the night. He was a fugitive from Justice and an outlaw and the six bullets that struck him were certainly well expended. Wm. Lang was a young man about 22 years of age and had been in that section of the country with his cattle about three months. In conversation with his father last evening, our reporter learned that the two came to Arizona from Kansas about five months ago. They are men of large capital, have had an extended experience in the stock business and intended putting about 10,000 head of cattle on their range had it not been for these border troubles. The son was bringing in some beef cattle for the Tombstone market when killed. *Mr. Lang leaves today to see that his son's body is properly buried and to move the cattle.*

It is certainly lamentable that the good should be slain with the bad and yet this was nothing more than was to be expected as a result of the raids from both sides of the line. For example we understand that a party of "rustlers" as they are called, went down into Mexico last month and rounded up some cattle. They were followed by the Mexicans who got so close upon them that they were obliged to abandon the stock. This was done in the vicinity of the late murders. The Mexicans took the stock and started back for home; at the same time picking up such cattle and horses as they chanced to meet. The stock was missed and a party of 16 Americans started in pursuit, overtook the Mexicans, had a fight with them, and retook the stock. This occurred during the latter part of July. If this is true, it is probable that the recent raiders were some of the same party defeated last month."

The Arizona Weekly Star, August 25, 1881, revealed later information.

"Border Warfare!"

The recent massacre in New Mexico

The Tombstone Nugget of the 16th inst., contains full details of the recent massacre of Americans in Guadalupe Canyon New Mexico. Parties who were on the ground within a few hours after the murders were committed, are now in Tombstone. The following is the story of one of them; John Gray, brother of one of the victims of the horrible tragedy:

"A party of seven started on the morning of the 12th from Lang's ranch with a band of cattle for the Tombstone market. They camped that night in Guadalupe Canyon, and in the morning, the 13th, at about sunrise, while all but two of the party were asleep, they were surprised by a party of 25 or 30 Mexicans, who opened fire upon them, and killed my brother, Dixie Lee Gray, Billy Lang, Old Man Clanton, Charley Snow and Jim Crane. Billy Byers was shot through the right arm and I think,

through the stomach, and he will probably die, if not already dead. The seventh man was known as "Harry." I don't remember his other name. He says after the firing commenced, he concealed himself behind a large bear bush and emptied two revolvers at the assailants. At this time, he was joined by Billy Lang, and they concluded to try and escape, and started to run, when the Mexicans opened a full volley at them and Billy fell. The bullets whistled all around him, one grazing the bridge of his nose, but he succeeded in getting away without any further injury and made his way back to Lang's ranch. Immediately upon his arrival there, the boys at the place hurried to the scene of the killing and found the bodies of the five men. They then commenced to search for Billy Byers and found that he had been taken in by the rancher near by, but had in a fit of delirium, again wandered off. In a short time they found him in an exhausted condition, and took him to Lang's ranch.

The D.L. Gray, mentioned as among the killed, was a son of Col. Mike Gray, well known in Tucson and also throughout California. The prevailing impression in Tombstone now is that the murders were committed by Mexican troops. It is known that a company of soldiers, under the command of Capt. Carrillo, were scouring the country in the vicinity of the scene of the massacre in search of a party of cowboys who had been depredating on Mexican soil. It is not unlikely that this affair may lead to serious complications between the two governments. At any rate, it will result in bloody border feuds between representatives of both nationalities, as the victims of the outrage were well known and have many friends and their deaths will not be allowed to pass unavenged."

The Arizona Weekly Star, September 1, 1881, printed even more:

"STORY OF AN EYEWITNESS"

"One of the ill-fated Lang party

tells how they were murdered."

"Billy Byers, one of the two who were fortunate to escape at the time of the murder of the Lang party, near the Chihuahua line, by Mexicans, came into Tombstone

Monday, bringing with him the wagon which the party had with them at the time. It had some 30 bullet holes in it, showing that a large number of shots were fired and that the attacking party were far from being good marksmen. Byers is rather under the medium size, has light hair, a fair complexion, and a quiet determined look. He came from Leavenworth, Kansas, last spring. A Nugget reporter interviewed Byers, who gave the following version of the killings.

We pitched our camp in a small swag between three low hills, which formed a sort of triangle around the camp, and at about daybreak the cattle appeared uneasy and showed signs of stampeding, when Will Lang said to Charlie Snow, who was guarding the cattle, "Charley, get your gun. I think there's a bear up there, and, if so, kill it." Charley then rode up one of the hills when the Mexicans opened fire, shooting him and pouring a volley into the camp. At the time they fired Dick Gray, Jim Crane, and myself had not got up, but Will Lang, 'Old Man' Clanton, and Harry Ernshaw were up or dressing. Gray, Crane, and Clanton were shot at the first fire, and almost instantly killed. When they first fired and killed Charley Snow I thought the boys were firing at a bear, jumped out of my blankets, and as I got up the boys around me were shot. As soon as I saw what was up, I looked for my rifle, and not seeing it, grabbed my revolver, and seeing them shooting at us from all sides, started to run, but had not gone forty feet when I was shot across my body, but I didn't fall, and in a few more steps was hit in my arm, knocked the pistol out of my hand and I fell down.

When I went down, Harry and Will passed me both running for the canyon. Soon Will fell, shot thru the legs and he then turned his revolved loose, and I think killed one Mexican and wounded another, as one man was killed and another badly wounded, and he was the only one that did much fighting.

You must remember that the reason we had no chance to fight was that the Mexicans had crawled up behind the low hills mentioned, and being almost over us fired right down among us. We could see nothing but little whiffs of smoke. Soon after, I saw some Mexicans coming from the direction Will and Harry had run, wearing their hats, and

Billy Byers

Wounded in Guadalupe Canyon, but lived to tell his story.

(Larry Byers photo, grandson of Billy)

then I thought they had been killed or had lost their hats in getting away.

When I saw the Mexicans begin stripping the bodies, I took off what clothes I had, even my finger ring, and lay stretched out with my face down and I was all bloody from my wounds, I thought they would pass me by thinking I was dead, and had already been stripped. I was not mistaken, for they never touched me, but as one fellow passed me on horseback he fired several shots at me, one grazing my head, and the others striking at my side, throwing dirt over me. But I kept perfectly still and he rode on. They stripped the bodies, cut open the valises, *took all the horses and saddles, and, in fact, everything they could, possibly getting altogether, including money, $2,000.*

The only way I can account for Harry's escape is that when Will began shooting at them, they turned most of their guns on him and that gave Harry a chance to get away. After they rode off I waited a long time, thinking they might come back or were watching. Finally, I crawled to where my pistol was and secured that, and then I heard someone and cocked my pistol determined to shoot if it was a Mexican, but it was one of the boys from the ranch, who having heard the shooting, rode over. He put me on his horse and took me over to the canyon, saying he would come back for me at night, but he didn't and I started for the ranch and was not found until the next day."

Byers told quite a story, one that showed him a master of quick thinking and sheer cold nerve to shed his clothes and lie still while they were shooting at him. At a later date he enhanced his story to include three men, who appeared to be in command, standing on a hill and providing direction to the others. He stated that he had no doubt that they were Mexican soldiers and he thought that they belonged to one of the companies stationed at Fronteras, as they buried one Mexican killed and took away another, badly wounded.

At a later time John Pleasant Gray wrote and left a manuscript, concerning the Guadalupe Canyon affair, with the Arizona Historical Society. The author includes excepts of information not included in previous accounts:

"A man by the name of Harry Ernshaw staggered into our camp in an exhausted condition, and it was some little time before he could tell the story.

He said he was with Lang's outfit, had come out from Tombstone with the object of buying some milk cows but not finding what he wanted, was returning with Lang's beef herd to Tombstone. They had driven the herd of one hundred steers into Guadalupe Canyon on Friday the day before, and made camp in the first clear spot they found which was near the rock monument which marks the four corners of Arizona, New Mexico, Sonora and Chihuahua.

It seems that during the night the herd stampeded and ran back up the canyon, and in rounding up the scattered herd some of the cowboys ran across my brother Dick, who had evidently been belated and had made camp. On learning of the trouble with the herd, Dick had saddled up and helped them drive the beeves back to camp. It seemed that a chain of circumstances was leading him blindly on to his fate.

Just before daylight, Charley Snow, a cowboy who was on herd, rode into camp and Ernshaw heard him tell the cook, "Old Man" Clanton, who was starting breakfast, that he felt sure a bear had frightened the cattle and he was going to circle around in the brush in the hope of getting a shot at it. This move of Snow's evidently started the trouble.

The Mexicans must have been concealed in the surrounding brush, and Snow probably rode right into them, for almost at once a volley of shots rang out, coming from all sides. Ernshaw had no gun and like most any tenderfoot in that position would have done, he just got up and ran. He did not know even the direction he took; he just kept going with his boots in his hand. He did not see what happened to the others, except "Old Man" Clanton, the cook, whom he saw fall face forward into the fire he had started for breakfast.

Our ranch was about fifteen miles from the place, and when Ernshaw staggered in about dusk, he must have gone many miles out of his way, as he said he had never paused in his flight except to stop a minute to pull on his boots. How he happened to find us must have been pure luck for he had never been there before. There were only two of us at the ranch as the house had been finished and the builders had returned sometime before to Tombstone. So our only recourse for help was to go to a new mining camp on the east slope of the Animas Mountains, called Gillespie, twenty miles away.

I rode horseback over there that night, finding twenty five miners at the camp. They, to the last man, nobly responded to my appeal for help. All had horses or mules to ride, and in scarcely no time at all were mounted and on the way back with me. We stopped at the ranch to get the wagon and team, loaded on the needed supplies, and pulled out for Guadalupe Canyon.

In a grassy glade, now so still and peaceful looked lay
four human bodies, probably just at the spots they had
been sleeping when the first fire of the attacking
Mexicans had caught them. All were perfectly nude, having evidently been stripped of all clothing by the
Mexicans. The only thing left of the camp outfit was the
buckboard standing near the ashes of the campfire, and
that was probably left because it would have been almost
impossible to take it over the mountain trail which the
Mexicans had to travel in order to reach their homes.

The dead lying there were: Billy Lang, cattle rancher; Jim
Crane, the outlaw; (Crane being on his way in to surrender to the sheriff as we had talked him into doing); "Old
Man Clanton, the cook mentioned before; and my brother, Dick - just turned nineteen. There were still two of
Lang's outfit missing and we spread out in search of
them. We found the dead body of Charley Snow, the man
who had told the cook he was going to look for the supposed bear. Evidently, he had made a gallant fight as his
body was riddled. He lay about a half mile from camp.
The other cowboy, Billy Byers, we found alive some five
miles away. He was shot thru the front of the abdomen
and the ball had gone clear thru his body, but evidently
not deep enough to penetrate any vital part, as he was
walking along in a dazed condition, completely out of his
head.

His wound was in a frightful condition from the heat and
the flies, but some of our miner friends knew what to do,
and they cleaned and dressed the wound.

With this wounded boy, all were present or accounted for.
We had to bury Charley Snow where we found his body
as it was too far gone to be moved. The other four bodies
and the wounded boy were placed in the wagon.

We took our dead back to the ranch and in coffins constructed of lumber for which we tore up the flooring with
the aid of our miner friends we buried the four bodies in
a little square plot on the top of a nearby knoll, render-
ing an equal and honorable reverence to all. Jim Crane,
the outlaw, had gone before a higher court and we were
no more his judges."

(Author's Note: This burial location was in the Animas
Valley, halfway between the ranches of Clanton and
Lang, about ten miles east of Cloverdale.)

As evidence of his opinion in this entire event, George Parsons wrote in his dairy on August 17, 1881:

"Am glad they killed him (Crane) - as for the others - if not guilty of cattle stealing, they had no business to be found in such company."

Jim and Tom Goldrup, Clanton relatives, state:

"Milt Joyce, owner of the Oriental saloon, believed that the Earps were anxious to silence Jim Crane before he got to Tombstone and that they were behind the ambush. That makes us wonder about the three men Byers saw standing on the hill, directing the ambush. Could it have been Wyatt, Morgan and Doc Holliday or, could it have been Captain Carrillo with two of his officers? We believe that Mexican soldiers were involved, but do not know for sure."

It was unbelievable that Byers, expecting to be killed at any second, could recognize the ambushers as Mexican from Fronteras. And all the while, he was playing dead. It was thoughtful of them to leave him his pistol. This massacre left a lot of unanswered questions at the time. It appears that most of the men in Clanton's camp just happened by and stayed the night. Ernshaw was out looking for milk cows and saw the camp. Gray was already camped alone, saw them gathering cattle and joined them. Then the most unusual appearance of all, a noted, wanted outlaw rode into camp at Midnight.

That puts together an entire string of unusual occurrences; an unarmed tenderfoot, a politician's son and a murderer, all riding about alone in the most dangerous spot in Arizona Territory and all three found the same camp! Isn't that an unusual coincidence?

A telegram from Dake to MacVeach, 2:31 A.M. August 5, 1881 reveals:

"FOLLOW DISPATCH JUST REC'D FROM TUCSON COWBOYS HAVE JUST MADE ANTOHER RAID INTO SONORA FRONTIER KILLING FOUR MEXICANS AND ROBBING THE OTHERS OF $4,000. THE MEXICAN AND GOVERNMENT IS VERY MUCH INCENSED AND THREATEN TO TAKE MATTERS INTO THEIR OWN HANDS IF THEY ARE

NOT PROTECTED BY OUR GOVERNMENT. SIGNED: J.W. EVANS, DEPUTY MARSHAL!"

'HAVE SENT DEPUTY AND POSSE AFTER COWBOYS. EXPENSE WILL BE FROM FIVE TO TEN THOUSAND DOL- LARS IF PURSUED UNTIL SUCCESSFUL. WHAT AMOUNT ALLOWED ON MY ESTIMATE FOR WITNESSES AND MARSHAL. SHALL BE GOVERNED IN REGARD TO MY EFFORTS IN THIS MATTER BY AMOUNT ALLOWED ON ESTIMATE OVER EXPENSE OF COURTS ABOUT TO CON- VENE. OWING TO WASH-OUTS ON THE RAILROAD, NO EASTERN MAIL REC'D HERE FOR PAST TEN DAYS. ANSWER C.P. DAKE."

Who did Crawley Dake trust most down in southeast Arizona? And who would he have head up the posse going after these Cowboys? Why, the Earp brothers, of course. The first area that this posse would search would be down in the Four Corner's area, where Arizona, New Mexico, Sonora, and Chihuahua all meet. Then, considering what lies in this area (Skeleton Canyon and Guadalupe Canyon) if the Earp posse was searching for these Cowboys it is only logical that they found them! They would have been most happy to have seen Jim Crane with them.

The night before THE GUNFIGHT. Doc Holliday lost his temper with Ike Clanton and told him that he had personally killed his old man with a Winchester and would do the same to him. In a later interview, Jim Earp would verify this statement.

That does a lot to explain why Ike and the Cowboys des- perately wanted Doc Holliday dead. They would do anything to accomplish this, except: face him.

An excerpt from the Sacramento Daily Record-Union, August 18, 1881, read:

> *"Great excitement has prevailed in Tombstone and vicin- ity for the past twenty-four hours. A large party has been raised to avenge the murders, headed by Mike Gray and Mr. Lang (sic) who had sons (sic) killed. The Clanton boys, whose father was murdered, also have raised a body of men, altogether numbering over 200 as desperate a gang, as could be imagined. They (made a) rendezvous at*

Soldier's Home (sic), 25 miles east of this city, and will carry the war into Mexico. Great apprehension is felt for Americans in Sonora, as it will more than likely be a war of retaliation. We are hourly expecting a collision. Mexican Troops, are in force on this line and will repel the invaders. Governor Fremont, being absent, there is no head to the American forces, and lawlessness seems to be the order of the day. Serious international complications will arise unless immediate steps are taken to put a stop to the movement on foreign soil. Blood will flow like water before another week rolls around."

The Record-Union, August 19, 1881, continued:

"Tombstone August 18th

"General Adolfo Dominguez has just arrived from the frontier of Sonora, where he holds the position of Adjutant under General Jose Otero, now in command of the troops on the Mexican frontier. General Dominguez said: 'Our people have been great sufferers. We have lost many citizens killed and much property stolen. We are therefore taking active steps to protect our citizens and repel raiders. There are 200 regulars, besides the militia, on the line, and three forts and supply camps are to be established at once. Every precaution will be taken to protect both our own citizens and such Americans as are engaged in legitimate industry within our lives. I hope to effect an arrangement by which a most thorough harmonious and efficient co-operation may exist between the American and Mexican troops operating on the border. We can only drive out these thieves and murderers by united action. We are not only willing but very anxious that such united action should exist.

Affairs have gradually been growing more desperate. It is estimated that within the last month more than ten citizens have been killed and upward of $20,000 worth of property taken.'

"Two companies of the Sixth Cavalry have been ordered from Camp Huachuca to Camp Grant, the nearest post to the scene of trouble.

General Otero has ordered Captain Carrillo, with his company, to the line where the raiders were expected to cross with their plunder, as the courier had ridden day and night, Captain Carrillo thought he must be some distance ahead of the raiders. It is not improbable that the killing in Guadalupe Canyon might have been done by the Mexican regulars under Captain Carrillo, as they were headed in that direction. Carrillo has about fifty men in his company."

It is apparent that the Mexican government meant business. Either the Americans would solve the problems caused by their outlaws or the Mexicans would and Crawley Dake did have an Earp posse in the Four Corners area. It would have been wise to use it.

(Author's Note: Following the death of "Old Man" Clanton and his cohorts, both Doc Holliday and Warren Earp disappeared from the Tombstone scene for a time. Strangely enough, on the way to the Gunfight at the O.K. Corral, Holliday carried a cane. Why? I have found no other time that he carried one. As to Warren Earp: many years ago, Al Turner showed me a letter written by Adelia Douglas Edwards, sister to the Earp brothers. In essence, this letter read, "my brother Warren missed the big fight in Tombstone because he was at my house recovering from a wound he received in a fight with rustlers down on the border.)

A reporter wrote about Warren in Gunnison, Colorado. Excerpts from the story follow:

"Do you see that man standing over there?" said a well known business man to a News-Democrat reporter yesterday, pointing to a rather tall well-dressed, pleasant looking stranger who stood leaning against the counter, tapping his boot with his cane, while he remained a silent listener to the conversation that was going on around him. "If you want an item, tackle him. If you can get him to talk he can give 'em to you - dead - oodles of them."

"Who is he?" asked the reporter, his curiosity somewhat aroused.

"That's Wyatt Earp, from Arizona, and there's his brother Warren, 'the Tiger' they call him, sitting over there. They don't look like bold bad men do they? Well, they're not, but you bet your life they've got the sand. I've known 'em for a long time now, and I'd just like you to takcle 'em

once. 'The Tiger' is a good one. He's a square man, but he will fight when necessary, and you just ought to see him turn himself loose. He'll just grab his two six-shooters and shut his eyes and wade in. He's a holy terror when he gets started. Wyatt is the general of the party, but the 'Tiger' is generally on hand when there's any fighting to be done."

"What are they doing here?" asked the reporter.

"Wyatt is a Deputy United States Marshal and is here on business partly, and then Tombstone got too hot for them just now. You see there's a big crowd of Cowboys out there that the Earp crowd has been fighting, and six of the Cowboys got killed within the last few months. Doc Holladay (sic) is a friend of the Earps and was with them in their fights, and that is why some of the people in Arizona were so anxious to get him back there. They didn't want to try him; not much. All they wanted was to get a hold of him once. None of these boys would object to going back and standing trial on any charges that could be brought against them, but they know that if they went back there now they would all be killed."

The reporter thought he would interview the 'Tiger' first. He found him a young man of perhaps twenty eight or thirty, with clear blue eyes and brown hair and mustache. He looked like anything but a fighter, and yet there was a look of firmness about the face that showed that the young man was not a man to fool with. He was neatly dressed and _walks_ _lame_ _from_ _the_ _effects_ _of_ _a_ _gun_ _shot_ _wound._

Twenty five years ago, the author did a great deal of "treasure hunting" along the border. When the Mexican people in the Fronteras vicinity were questioned about the Guadalupe Canyon massacre, they vehemently insisted that their people would not do such a thing. Besides, at that time, they feared retaliation from the Cowboy gangs found along the border and from the American army. They were sincere in believing that other Americans committed the deed.

Author's summation of the Guadalupe Canyon massacre:

Doc Holliday was carrying a cane the day of the Gunfight at O.K. Corral on October 26, 1881, just two months and thirteen days after the massacre in Guadalupe Canyon. He was not in the habit of sporting a cane, so he must have had it for a reason. And, as he did not carry it again after October 26, 1881, it is apparent that he no longer needed it. About three months is the length of time it takes a bullet wound to heal if nothing serious is hit.

Warren Earp missed the big fight in Tombstone because of a bullet wound he had received earlier from rustlers down on the border; according to his sister. The only incident where he could have been wounded and in the time factors right is Guadalupe Canyon.

When the Earp federal posse rode out of Tombstone Doc Holliday and Warren Earp rode with them. When they rode back into town neither man was with them. Both men disappeared; Doc going east on the train and Warren going west to his sister's house. Evidently, Doc's wound was less serious than Warren's as he was back in a few weeks.

Several Mexicans were at the massacre scene as the only eye witness (Byers) reports them there. The three men standing on a hill were Captain Carrillo and his officers. They were there to witness and report to their government that the Americans were making a significant effort to do something about the Cowboy faction raiding into Mexico, in order to correct the border problems.

Two facts are certain: (1) there was an Earp posse in the four corners area at that time, and (2) there was a troop of Mexican cavalry led by Capitan Carrillo in that same area, but just below the border.

Sherman McMasters, who usually acted as a scout because he was familiar with the country, sighted the dust made by a herd of cattle, late in the afternoon of August 12th. When he

<u>Billy Lang</u>
Killed in Guadalupe Canyon

(Larry Byers photo)

saw that "Old Man" Clanton was with them he wasted no more time, but hurried back to the posse with the news. Wyatt and Doc rode back with him and concealing themselves in the rocks, verified that it was Clanton through binoculars. They assumed that anyone with Clanton was sure to be a rustler so they rode back to camp, planning their attack as they rode.

Shortly before daybreak, the Earp posse moved into their positions. By the time they had done this Capitan Carrillo and two of his officers had moved to a vantage point where they could view the proceedings that were about to begin. A squad of soldiers were concealed behind a low hill nearby.

As these movements transpired Will Lang noticed that the cattle were becoming restless. He said to Charley Snow, "Charley, there must be a bear out there. He's spooking the cattle. Take your rifle and kill it!"

Snow went up a small hill and right into that squad of Mexican soldiers concealed behind it. By the time that Snow realized they were there they had riddled him with bullets.

"Old Man" Clanton was up building a breakfast fire and at the sound of the rifle, stood up to look right at Doc Holliday. Doc knew that now was the time or all would be lost. He raised his rifle and shot Clanton dead center. Clanton fell forward into his breakfast fire. The rest of the Earp posse opened fire and a hail of lead swept the rustler's camp.

Snow, Gray, Crane, and Clanton were shot at the first fire. Harry Ernshaw and Will Lang ran for the canyon. They passed Billy Byers, who was also running. Byers was hit in the stomach and the arm, knocking him down. He said that Lang was shot through both legs, but fought from a ground position until he was killed. Byers said that Lang was the only one of them who managed to do any fighting.

When the firing ceased the Mexicans moved in and began to strip the bodies. Their mission accomplished, the Earp posse rode away, leaving the Mexicans to gather whatever loot they desired. They had two of their own wounded to care for.

Graves of Billy Byers and his wife, Minnie in the Lebanon Cemetery a few miles north of Cortez, Colorado. Byers, though wounded, was one of the two men who survived the Guadalupe Canyon massacre on August 13, 1881.

(Courtesy J.A. Browning)

Chapter VII

I PLUGGED HIM MYSELF!

On the night of September 8, 1881, the Bisbee stage was robbed near Hereford. The bandits took $2,500 that was in the Well's Fargo box and $750 in cash and jewelry from the four passengers.

Levy McDaniels was the stage driver and there was no guard along. When two men, brandishing weapons, stepped into the road Levy stopped the horses and wisely offered no resistance. Later, he identified the man who robbed the passengers as Pete Spencer, and his partner as Frank Stilwell, one of Sheriff Behan's deputies. There were other men in the brush, but it was too dark for him to tell who they were.

The next morning, shortly after the robbery was reported to the Tombstone Well's Fargo office, Wyatt and Morgan Earp, Fred Dodge and Marshall Williams rode to Hereford to question Levy McDaniels. Two other representatives of the law, Dave Neagle and Billy Breakenridge, were sent out by Sheriff Behan.

In Hereford, Wyatt discovered that Curly Bill, Stilwell, and Pony Diehl had been together all day the day before. Early that same night Pete Spencer had joined them, and all four of them had ridden out the Bisbee Road.

Breakenridge and Neagle joined the other posse in Hereford. However, after they had trailed the culprits for awhile they decided that their quarry had headed for Bisbee, so they split off from the others and rode straight for Bisbee.

After carefully studying the crime scene, especially the boot tracks, the Earp party rode into Bisbee. In Bisbee, Wyatt went to the shoe shop. There he found that Stilwell had purchased new heels for his boots. When Wyatt carefully examined the discarded bootheels he felt certain that they matched those seen at the holdup site. The cobbler also told Wyatt that Spencer and Stilwell had ridden into town together.

The two suspects were arrested by Wyatt and Morgan Earp, Billy Breakenridge and Marshall Williams. Stilwell was not only a deputy sheriff, but also a partner with Sheriff Behan in a Charleston livery stable.

Justice Wells Spicer granted them bail in the sum of $7,000 each - $5,000 for robbing the mail and $2,000 for robbing the passengers. Money for their bail was raised quickly.

The fact that a deputy sheriff was moonlighting by robbing stages was a bit of a surprise - but quite understandable when the September 15, 1881, Epitaph revealed who went their bail:

"Frank Stilwell and Pete Spencer furnished bail yesterday in the sum of $14,000 upon the two charges of highway robbery and robbing the United States mail. In the former the bail was $2,000 and in the latter $5,000 each. The sureties in both cases were Ham Light, William Allen, and Ike Clanton."

The September 13, 1881, Epitaph commented:

"The Epitaph has no desire to prejudge the case, but if it turns out as now anticipated, that the officers of the law are implicated in this nefarious business, it would seem to be in order for Sheriff Behan to appoint another deputy."

It would appear to the author that Stilwell was overworked. He owned partnerships in livery stables in Charleston and Bisbee, served as a deputy sheriff in both places and still found time to rob stagecoaches.

Both Stilwell and Spencer vowed to get even with the Earp posse. While Wyatt was in Tucson for Spencer's and Stilwell's federal arraignment, Morgan, while crossing Allen Street was accosted by Ringo, Frank and Tom McLaury, Milt Hicks, Joe Hill, and Ike and Billy Clanton. Frank McLaury said, "You Earps may have arrested Stilwell and Spencer, but if you ever come after a McLaury, I'll kill you!"

Morgan was alone and unarmed, but he didn't even lose his temper (which was remarkable for Morgan). He didn't raise his voice, as he calmly replied, "If the Earps come after you, they'll get you," and continued on across Allen Street.

Ike and Billy Clanton and Frank and Tom McLaury had breakfast together at Jack Chandler's milk ranch on the morning of October 25, 1881. Following the morning meal, Ike and Tom hitched up the buckboard to go into Tombstone for supplies. Before they had departed Chandler's, the men had agreed to meet in Tombstone at the Grand Hotel bar the next day (October 26th).

Billy Clanton and Frank McLaury stayed in the vicinity of Antelope Springs, rounding up cattle. They rode into Tombstone from there the next day, *NOT FROM CHARLESTON*, as some reports states.

Soon after Wyatt had returned from Tucson, he was accosted by a highly irate Ike Clanton, who was terror-stricken that the word was out that he was willing to sell out his outlaw friends for the Well's Fargo reward.

Right on Allen Street he accused Wyatt of telling Doc Holliday about their agreement to capture Head and Leonard. Wyatt denied that he had done so and insisted that they go find Holliday to verify that he had not been told.

When they located Holliday, Ike, in fear and anger, babbled the entire story while on the street and before several suddenly interested spectators. Of course, Doc had not the slightest idea of what he was talking about until he had babbled the whole story.

Doc's response was "You double crossing bastard!"

Ike was right. His cohorts in crime had found out that he

had tried to sell them out. They had about a belly full of Ike anyway. Their plan was to do away with the Earps and Holliday using Ike as the magnet. If they happened to get Ike in the process, why that would be all right too.

On the night of October 25, 1881, Ike was in the Occidental Lunch Room, which was attached to the Alhambra Saloon, when Morgan and Doc came in. Wyatt was already there, sitting in the back. Both Ike and Doc were carrying an overload of whiskey, and soon talked themselves into a yelling, cursing fight, each screaming obscenities.

Doc's anger knew no bounds because of the threats the Cowboys had made against him and the Earps. With his hand under his coat, Doc cursed Ike as a "son-of-a-bitch cowboy," and urged him to use his gun. Ike claimed that he was not armed.

"You son-of-a-bitch, if you're not, go get heeled!" Holliday exploded. "Your damned big mouth has already got your old man killed! I plugged him myself, and I'd be happy to do the same to you!"

Morgan, who had been sitting on the counter nearby, spoke up, "Yeah, you son-of-a-bitch, you can get all the fight you want right now!"

Wyatt walked up to the group, but said nothing. Virgil and Deputy Marshal James Flynn were just outside the door.

Still in shock over the things that Doc had said to him, Ike left, asking that he not be shot in the back. Such a statement was ridiculous. Neither Holliday nor the Earps ever shot anyone in the back - not even someone like Ike Clanton.

Morgan went up Allen Street to the Oriental Saloon; Ike went to the Grand Hotel, and Wyatt went to the Crystal Palace Saloon, where he had a faro table. In a short while he came back out on Allen Street and was confronted once more by Ike Clanton. He told Wyatt that when Doc had invited him to reach for his gun, he "had not been fixed right," but, that in the morning it would be man-to-man and that it was high time that the fighting talk be fetched to a close. His last words to Wyatt were: "You must not think I won't be after you all in the morning."

"I would fight no one if I can get away from it, because there is no money in it," Wyatt replied. Then, carrying his faro bank money, Wyatt walked west on Allen Street. He met Holliday near the Alhambra and they walked down Allen together, until Doc broke off to go to his room at Fly's. Wyatt continued on to his house. (Holliday never lived in a house and never owned one in Tombstone through some of the "overnight" historians tell visitors, "that's Doc Holliday's house!")

That same night (October 25th) a strange poker game took place in the Occidental. The participants of this game were Virgil Earp, John Behan, Tom McLaury, and another man who has not been identified. Ike Clanton came later and they gave him a seat. These men played poker all night. As was usual, Ike had a complaint. He was upset this time because Virgil had held a pistol on his lap during the whole game. (This only indicates how much Virgil trusted these men.) Virgil started home about 6:00 A.M. Ike called to him and asked him to carry a message to Doc Holliday. "Tell that damned son-of-a-bitch he has to fight!"

"I'm going home to bed. Don't you create any disturbance!" Virgil replied.

As Virgil walked away, Ike yelled back, "you may have to fight before you know it!"

Virgil went home and went to bed - but around 9:00 A.M. Officer Bronk woke Virgil to tell him that Ike Clanton was on the streets threatening to shoot him on sight. Ike's threats did not much concern Virgil and he went back to sleep.

When Virgil did start uptown he met a man, named Lynch, who gave him the same report.

A little before noon Ike appeared at Fly's Boarding House, where Doc lived. "Big Nose" Kate was visiting Doc at the time and Mrs. Fly told her that Ike had been there looking for Doc.

When Kate informed Doc, he replied, "If God will let me live long enough, he will see me!"

By this time Virgil was up and dressed, and he and Morgan had gone to locate Ike. The two men went up Allen Street to Fifth Street, then north to Fremont, then turned west to Fourth Street where they found Ike in an alley.

Virgil said, "I hear you are hunting some of us." Ike swung his Winchester toward Virgil who grabbed the rifle, then hit Ike over the head with his pistol. Morgan and Virgil took Ike's rifle and pistol away from him. Then they took him to Justice Wallace's court. (This was not at the courthouse on Fremont, but the J.P.'s office on Fourth Street between Allen and Toughnut.)

While they were waiting for the judge, Ike said, "I will get even with all of you for this. If I had a six-gun I would make a fight with all of you!"

Morgan said, "If you want to make a fight right bad, I will give you one," and offered Ike his own pistol. Ike started to get up, but Deputy Sheriff Campbell pushed him back saying that he wouldn't allow any trouble.

Justice Wallace fined Ike $25 and $2.50 court costs, for a total of $27.50, for carrying a concealed weapon.

Ike admitted that he was armed and LOOKING FOR DOC HOLLIDAY. (IT IS OBVIOUS THAT HOLLIDAY WAS AT THE TOP OF THE ASSASSINATION LIST.) He said that Virgil struck him from behind, and that when he recovered, Morgan had a pistol stuck in his face. Virgil said that he asked Ike if he was hunting for him and Ike replied, "I was, and if I had seen you a second before, the coroner would have had extra work!"

Six people would later testify that they heard Ike making threats to kill Holliday and the Earps. They were R.F. Hafford, E.F. Boyle, Julius A. Kelly, Virgil, Wyatt, and "Big Nose" Kate.

By this time Wyatt was sick and tired of the Cowboy threats and posturing, so he said to Ike, "You damned cur thief, you have been threatening our lives and I know it. I think I would be justified in shooting you down anyplace I should meet you, but if you are anxious to make a fight I will go anywhere on earth to make a fight with you, even over to the San Simon among your crowd!"

Ike replied, "All right, I'll see you after I get through here. I only want four feet of ground to fight on!"

Wyatt left the justice's office very angry, and went outside where he encountered Tom McLaury, who made a very serious mistake by saying, "If you want to make a fight, I will fight you anywhere!"

"All right, make a fight right here!" Wyatt thundered. At the same time he slapped Tom in the face with his left hand and drew his pistol with his right. Tom had a pistol on his hip, but made no move toward it, even when Wyatt told him, "jerk your gun and use it!" He made no reply and Wyatt hit him over the head with his gun barrel, then walked away and left him lying in the street. Wyatt walked over to Hafford's corner, got himself a cigar - then stood by the front door, watching the Cowboys. Soon Billy Clanton and both McLaury brothers went down Fourth Street to Spangenberger's Gun Shop. Wyatt followed them down and saw Frank McLaury's horse standing on the sidewalk with his head in the gun shop. He started backing the horse off the walk when the McLaurys and Billy Clanton came to the door - the latter with his hand on his pistol. Wyatt said, "You will have to get this horse off the sidewalk." Frank McLaury backed his horse off the walk and all four of the Cowboys went into the gun shop. Wyatt, looking through the door, could see them putting cartridges into their shell belts.

About this time, the Citizen's Safety Committee came to Virgil and offered to back him up with men and guns. Virgil thanked them, but refused their help, saying it was his job to disarm the Cowboys and he wanted no help except that of his brothers.

There have always been questions concerning the legal status of Wyatt, Morgan, and Holliday at the time of the gunfight.

Virgil said this under oath:

"Wyatt Earp had been sworn in to act in my place while I was in Tucson, and on my return, his saloon (Oriental) was opened and I appointed him a "Special," to keep the peace, with power to make arrests, and also called on him on the 26th to assist me in disarming those parties: Ike Clanton, Billy Clanton, Tom McLaury, and Frank McLaury."

"Morgan Earp had been sworn in as a Special Policeman and wore a badge with "Special Police" engraved on it, and he had been sworn in and acted as a "Special" for about a month."

"As for John H. Holliday - I called on him that day for assistance to help disarm the Clantons and the McLaurys."

Standing before Hafford's Saloon, Virgil turned to Wyatt, Morgan, and Doc Holliday and said, "Come on, and help me disarm them." They went down Fourth Street to Fremont then west to Fly's studio. Here they met Sheriff John Behan, whose first two statements described him completely. The first one denied the second. The first was, "For God's sake, don't go down there or you will get murdered!" The second was, "I have disarmed them!" Now, if he had really disarmed the Cowboys, how could they have murdered the Earps and Doc Holliday - talked them to death?

But, evidently, Wyatt wasn't listening either. He had been carrying his pistol in his hand. At Behan's words he put it back in his pocket.

Mason's Western Hotel in Contention

Contention mine works in Tombstone

"Honest John" Montgomery

Chapter VIII

GUNFIGHT AT O.K. CORRAL - six, seven & eight

On the windy, extremely cold and disagreeable afternoon of October 26, 1881, guns roared and thundered at "Honest John" Montgomery's O.K. Corral for several seconds, then suddenly silence reigned, leaving three men dead and two others seriously injured. (The fight actually started on the east half of Lot Number 2, Block 17, owned by W.A. Harwood, and was not part of the O.K. Corral, owned by John Montgomery and Edward Monroe Benson at that time. At the present time that area has been made part of the O.K. Corral.)

This famous battle lasted less than thirty seconds, yet the controversy arising as to its particulars has endured well over a century. The names of the participants have become immortal in western folklore, legend, and history.

The three Earps; Wyatt, Morgan and Virgil, and their friend, Doc Holliday, met in front of Hafford's Saloon (located on the northeast corner of Allen and Fourth Streets) and discussed their plan of action. Then the four of them spread out and walked down Fourth Street to Fremont, to the O.K. Corral, and into the bloody pages of Tombstone history.

The best and most accurate account may be obtained from the files of the Tombstone Epitaph:

> *"Stormy as were the early days of Tombstone, nothing ever occurred equal to the event of yesterday. Since the retirement of Ben Sippy as marshal and the appointment of V.W. Earp to fill the vacancy, the town has been noted for its quietness and good order. The fractious and much*

dreaded cowboys, when they came to town, were on their good behavior and no unseemly brawls were indulged in, and it was hoped by our citizens that no more such deeds would occur as led to the killing of Marshal White one year ago. This time it struck with its full and awful force upon those who, heretofore, have made the good name of this county a by word and a reproach, instead of upon some officer in the discharge of his duty of a peaceable and unoffending citizen."

"Since the arrest of Stilwell and Spencer for the robbery of the Bisbee stage, there have been oft repeated threats conveyed to the Earp brothers - Virgil, Wyatt, and Morgan - that the friends of the accused, or in other words, the cowboys, would get even with them for the part they have taken in the pursuit and arrest of Stilwell and Spencer. The active part of the Earps in going after stage robbers, beginning with the one last spring where Budd Philpot lost his life, and the more recent one near Contention, has made them exceedingly obnoxious to the bad element of this county and put their lives in jeopardy every month."

"Sometime Tuesday, Ike Clanton came into town and during the evening had some little talk with Doc Holliday and Marshal Earp but nothing to cause either to suspect, further than their general knowledge of the man and the threats that had previously been conveyed to the Marshal, that the gang intended to clean out the Earps, that he was thirsting for blood at this time with one exception and that was that Clanton told the Marshal, in answer to a question, that the McLaurys were in Sonora. Shortly after this occurrence someone came to the Marshal and told him that the McLaurys had been seen a short time before just below town. Marshal Earp, now knowing what might happen and feeling his responsibility for the peace and order of the city, stayed on duty all night and added to the police force his brother, Morgan, and Holliday. The night passed without any disturbance whatever and at sunrise he went home and retired to rest and sleep. A short time afterwards one of his officers, named Bronk, came to his house and told him that Clanton was hunting him with threats of shooting him on sight. He discredited the report and did not get out of bed. Sometime later he dressed and went with his brother Morgan uptown. It was not long before another man,

Lynch, reported to him the same thing. They walked down Allen Street to Fifth, crossed over to Fremont and down to Fourth, where, upon turning up Fourth toward Allen, they came upon Clanton with a Winchester rifle in his hand and a revolver on his hip. The marshal walked up to him, grabbed the rifle and hit him a blow on the head at the same time, stunning him so that he was able to disarm him without further trouble. He marched Clanton off to the police court, fined Clanton $25 and costs making $27.50 altogether. This occurrence must have been about 1 o'clock in the afternoon."

R.F. Coleman, whose eyewitness account was published in the Tombstone Epitaph, appears to have changed his story somewhat as his story and his testimony do not completely agree.

Coleman's story in the Epitaph said:

"I was in the O.K. Corral at 2:30 P.M. when I saw the two Clantons (Ike and Bill) and the two McLaurys (Frank and Tom) in an earnest conversation across the street in Dunbar's Corral. I went up the street and notified Sheriff Behan and told him it was his duty, as sheriff, to go and disarm them. I told him they had gone to the West End Corral. I then went and saw Marshal Virgil Earp and notified him to the same effect. I then met Billy Allen and we walked through the O.K. Corral, about fifty yards behind the sheriff. On reaching Fremont Street I saw Virgil Earp, Wyatt Earp, Morgan Earp, and Doc Holliday, in the center of the street, all armed. I had reached Bauer's Meat Market. Johnny Behan had just left the cowboys, after having a conversation with them. I went along to Fly's Photograph Gallery, when I heard Virgil Earp say, 'Give up your arms or throw up your hands!' there was some reply made by Frank McLaury, when firing became general, over thirty shots being fired. Tom McLaury fell first, but raised and fired again before he died. Bill Clanton fell next, and raised to fire again when Mr. Fly took his revolver from him. Frank McLaury ran a few yards and fell, Morgan Earp was shot through and fell. Doc Holliday was hit in the left hip, but kept firing. Virgil Earp was hit in the third or fourth fire, in the leg which staggered him, but he kept up his effective work. Wyatt Earp stood up and fired in rapid succession, as cool as a

cucumber, and was not hit. Doc Holliday was as calm as though at target practice and fired rapidly. After the firing was over, Sheriff Behan went up to Wyatt Earp and said, "I'll have to arrest you." Wyatt replied, "I won't be arrested today. I am right here and I'm not going away. You have deceived me. You told me these men were disarmed! I went to disarm them."

R.F. Coleman was an incurable gossip and spent a great deal of his time running about town fabricating fantastic tales to make himself look important. He told so many versions of the fight that even he could not remember if any of them were correct. Even today, when anyone is referred to as R.F. Coleman, it is a mark of ridicule. From his position at Bauer's Market the only part of the fight he could have seen was the portion of it that took place in Fremont Street.

"This ends Mr. Coleman's story which in the most essential particulars has been confirmed by others. Marshal Earp says that he and his party met the Clantons and the McLaurys in the alleyway by the McDonald place; he called to them to throw up their hands, that he had come to disarm them. Instantaneously Bill Clanton and one of the McLaury's fired, and then it became general. Mr. Earp says it was the first shot from Frank McLaury that hit him. (Note that Virgil said that Frank McLaury shot him and he should know better than anyone. The only other candidate to have shot him was Billy Clanton. Had Billy shot him from his position his shin bone would have been shattered. The shot had to have come from the side to wound Virgil in such a manner and Frank was the only one in that position.) In other particulars his statement does not materially differ from the statement given. Ike Clanton was not armed and ran across to Allen Street and took refuge in the dance hall there. The two McLaurys and Bill Clanton all died within a few minutes after being shot. The Marshal was shot through the calf of his right leg, the ball going clear through. His brother Morgan, was shot through the shoulders, the ball entering the point of the right shoulder blade, following across the back, shattering off a piece of one vertebrae and passing out the left shoulder in about the same position that it entered the right. (Note that the path of the bullet was in a horizontal path. That means that the only per-

son that could have shot him was Tom McLaury - across his saddle. Both Billy Clanton and Frank McLaury were in a position such that their shots would have followed a trajectory of an upward angle - not horizontal.) The wound is dangerous but not necessarily fatal, and Virgil's is far more painful than dangerous. Doc Holliday was hit upon the scabbard of his pistol, the leather breaking the force of the ball so that no material damage was done other than to make him limp a little in his walk."

"Dr. Matthews impaneled a coroner's jury who went and viewed the bodies as they lay in the cabin in the rear of Dunbar's Stables and then adjourned until 10 o'clock this morning."

(The coroner chose a strange body of people when he impaneled a jury for the inquest. Matthews chose mostly Cowboys or Cowboy sympathizers: Ike Clanton, William Claiborne, C.H. Light, John Behan, R.F. Coleman, William Cuddy, Peter Fallehy, and Mrs. Martha King.)

The Nugget, also a Tombstone paper, managed to obtain part of Dr. Matthews testimony:

"...they (the McLaurys and Clanton) died from the affects of pistol and gunshot wounds; there were two wounds on the body (Clanton); did not examine them thoroughly; there was one two inches from the left nipple, penetrating the lungs; the other was beneath the twelfth rib, above and beneath, six inches to the right of the navel; think neither of the wounds went through the body; not probing the wounds, cannot positively say what direction they took; both were in front through the body; my opinion at that time was that those wounds were the cause of death; examined the body of Frank McLaury at the same time and day; found in the body of Frank McLaury one wound, penetrating the abdomen one inch to the left of the navel...I examined the body of Tom McLaury at the same time and place; found on his body twelve buckshot wounds - on the right side of the body, near together, under the arms, between the third and fifth ribs; my opinion was that they were buckshot wounds; laid the palm of my hand on them; it would cover the whole of them, about four inches in space..."

After two hours of deliberation the coroner's jury rendered

R.F. Hafford & Co.

(Fly)

The Earps & Holliday left the front
of Hafford's to go to the site of the gunfight.

O.K. Corral - as it looked in the 1880's

its verdict saying that the McLaurys and Billy Clanton came to their deaths at the hands of the Earp brothers and Doc Holliday. The verdict did not meet with general approval as it did not state whether or not the shooting was justifiable.

> *"On Saturday the warrants for the arrest of Wyatt, Virgil, and Morgan Earp and J.H. "Doc" Holliday were placed in the hands of the sheriff but as Morgan and Virgil Earp were confined to their beds through wounds received in the late street fight, the warrants were not in their cases served and only Wyatt and Holliday were placed under arrest. When these persons were taken before Judge Spicer he at first denied bail, but upon showing of the facts by affidavits, bail was granted and fixed in the sum of $20,000 each for each of the defendants, which amount was furnished."*

> *"Today Holliday and Wyatt Earp were before Justice Spicer to answer the charge. The investigation was conducted with closed doors. No one, except the officers of the court, and the witness whose testimony was being taken up, were allowed inside. The investigation is not yet concluded and will probably occupy the court for several days."*

Following the gunfight the Nugget printed this statement:

> *"The 26th of October, 1881, will always be marked as one of the crimson days in the annals of Tombstone, a day when blood flowed as water, and human life was held as a shuttle cock, a day to be remembered as witnessing the bloodiest and deadliest street fight that has ever occurred in this place, or probably in the Territory."*

The Epitaph statement was:

> *"The feeling among the best class of our citizens is that the Marshal was entirely justified in his efforts to disarm these men, and that being fired upon they had to defend themselves which they did most bravely."*

Regardless of the differences of opinion, the day after the fight the bodies were dressed in expensive store clothes, placed in fine caskets, and put on public view at the Ritter and Ream funeral parlor. A large sign: **MURDERED IN THE STREETS OF TOMBSTONE**, was placed above the bodies lying in state.

The two McLaurys rode to their last resting place in a hearse together while Billy Clanton rode in another alone.

An October 28, 1881, issue of the Epitaph describes the funeral:

> *"The funeral of the McLaury brothers and Clanton yesterday was numerically one of the largest ever witnessed in Tombstone. It took place at 3:30 from the undertaking parlor of Messers. Ritter and Ream. The procession, headed by the Tombstone brass band, moved down Allen Street and thence to the cemetery. The sidewalks were densely packed for three to four blocks. The body of Clanton was in the first hearse, and those of the two McLaury brothers in the second, side by side, and were interred in the same grave. It was a most impressive and saddening sight and such a one as it is to be hoped may never occur again in this community."*

On November 2, 1881, Sheriff Johnny Behan gave his testimony:

> *"About 2:30 I was in the barber's shop and heard of trouble between the Clantons and the Earps. I went over to Hafford's Corner. I asked Virgil Earp, the marshal, what was the excitement. He said there was a lot of _____ in town looking for a fight. He mentioned no names. I said to Earp, "You had better disarm the crowd." He said he would not, but would give them a chance to make a fight. I said, "It is your duty as a peace officer to disarm the parties." I meant any parties connected with the cowboys who had arms. Morgan Earp and Holliday were the ones I was talking to at the intersection of Allen and Fourth. Virgil Earp had a shotgun. I saw no arms on the others. I then went down Fourth Street to the corner of Fremont and crossed to the opposite side of Fourth Street and saw Frank McLaury holding a horse and in conversation with somebody. I told McLaury I would have to disarm him; that there was likely to be some trouble in town and I proposed to disarm everybody that had an arm. He said that he would not give up his gun, that he didn't intend to have any trouble. I insisted. About that time I saw Ike Clanton and Tom McLaury down the street below Fly's building. I said to Frank, "Come with me." We went down to where Ike Clanton and Tom McLaury were standing. I said to them, "Boys, you must give up your arms."*

Billy Clanton and William Claiborne, alias Billy the Kid, were also there. Frank McLaury demurred. Ike Clanton told us he was unarmed. I put my arm around his waist and found that he was not armed. Tom McLaury pulled his coat open and showed that he was not armed. I saw five standing there and asked how many there were in their party. They said four. Claiborne said he was not one of them; that he was there wanting them to leave town. I said, "Boys, you must go up to the sheriff's office, lay aside your guns and stay until I get back." I told them I was going to disarm the other party. At that time I saw the Earps and Holliday coming down the south side of Fremont Street. They came by the post office and Bauer's shop. I mean Morgan Earp and Doc Holliday. I said to the Clanton party, "I see them coming down; wait here; I will go up and stop them." I walked twenty-two or twenty-three steps up the street and met them as they were coming out from under the awning at Bauer's shop and told them not to go any further, that I was there for the purpose of disarming the Clanton party. They did not heed me. I said, "Go back! I'm not going to allow any trouble if I can help it!" They brushed past me and I turned and went with them or followed them, expostulating. When they arrived within a few feet of the Clantons and McLaurys, I heard one of them say, I think it was Wyatt Earp, "You s___ of _____s, you have been looking for a fight and now you can have it!" About this time a voice said, "Throw up your hands!" During this time pistols were pointed. I saw a nickel-plated pistol in particular. It was in the hands of the Earp party. I think Doc Holliday. It was pointed, I think , at Billy Clanton. I am not certain that Holliday had it. When the order was given to "throw up your hands," I heard Billy Clanton say, "Don't shot me. I don't want to fight." At the same time, Tom McLaury threw open his coat and said "I have nothing," or "I am not armed," or words to that effect, making the same remark and gesture he had previously made to me. I don't remember the position of Billy Clanton's hands. My attention was directed on the nickel-plated pistol for a couple of seconds. The nickel-plated pistol was the first fired and almost instantaneously came two shots right together. The first two shots could not have been fired from the same pistol. They were too close together. The nickel-plated pistol was fired by the second man from the right. After the first two or three shots were fired very rapidly the firing was general. The first two shots were fired by the Earp party. I thought the next three shots came from the same side, but was not certain. It was only my impression. After the words, "throw up your hands," immediately the nickel-plated pistol went off. I saw Frank McLaury with one hand to his belly and with his right hand shooting toward Morgan Earp. As he started across the street I heard a couple of shots from the direction in which Frank McLaury went. I looked and saw him running and a shot was fired and he went over on his head. I heard Morgan Earp say, "I got him." There may have been a couple of shots afterwards but that was the end of the fight. I did not see the effects of the first two shots that were fired; the only parties I saw fall were Frank McLaury and Morgan Earp. I saw no effects from the next three shots. The first man I thought was hit was Frank McLaury. I saw him staggering and bewildered after the first five shots. I never saw any arms in the hands of any body of the McLaury or Clanton party. Frank McLaury was the first man in whose hands I saw the pistol. After the first few shots Ike Clanton broke and ran. I saw him at the corner of Fly's house running into the back building.

When Ike Clanton broke and ran I did not know where he went. I found him afterwards in Emmanuel's building on Tough Nut Street. I saw a shotgun with Holliday before the fight commenced, as they were coming down the street. He had it under his coat. I did not see the gun go off and if I heard it, I did not distinguish it from a pistol. I afterwards examined Billy Clanton, before he died, as he was lying in the street. After he was taken in the house all I heard him say was to go away and let him die. I saw him lying on the sidewalk and saw him when he shot Morgan Earp. A number were in the room when Billy was carried in. Dr. Gilberson said it was no use to give him anything. I left before Billy Clanton died. Tom McLaury's body was in the same room."

(Most of Behan's testimony may be discounted as by his own admission elsewhere he was hiding most of the fight and could not see what was happening.)

Although Virgil Earp was never arrested, he did testify. His story of the morning of October 26th was:

"When I met Lynch, on the morning or noon of the 26th of October, he told me to look out for Ike Clanton; that he was armed and hunting for me, and allowed he would kill me on sight.

The first man that spoke to me about any threats was Officer Bronk; I was down home, in bed, when he called. He came down after a commitment that I had for a party that was in jail. This was about 9 o'clock in the morning of October 26th. He said to me, 'you had better get up, there is liable to be h—l to pay; Clanton is threatening to kill Holliday as soon as he gets up; he says he's counting you fellows in, too,' meaning the Earp brothers. That is all he said.

The next man was Lynch. I have stated what he said.

The next man I saw were Morgan and James Earp. One of them asked me if I had seen Ike Clanton. I said no. One of them said he had a Winchester rifle and a six-shooter, and that he was threatening to kill us on sight. I asked Morgan if he had any idea where we could find him. He said he did not. I told him to come and go with me and we would hunt him up and arrest and disarm him.

Several men came to me on Allen Street between Fourth and Fifth Streets, men whose names I do not know, who warned me to be careful, and said, 'If you turn your backs on that party you will get killed; they are going to make a fight.' This was after Ike Clanton's arrest, and before the fight. One man in particular came to me and said, "Ain't you liable to have trouble? I told him I didn't know, it looked kind of that way, but I couldn't tell. He says, 'I see two more of them just rode in; Ike Clanton walked to them, and was telling them about your hitting him over the head with a six-shooter.'

He says that one of them that rode in that had a horse said, "Now is the time to make a fight.' This was after the arms of Ike Clanton had been deposited in the Grand Hotel. While this man was finishing his say Bob Hatch came up within ten feet of me and motioned to me as if he wanted to speak to me. He says, 'For God's sake, hurry down to the gunshop; they are all down there, and Wyatt is all alone; they are liable to kill him before you get there.' I went down there to the gunshop. A man by the name of W.B. Murray, and a man named J.L. Fonck came to me at separate times and each said in substance, 'I know you are going to have trouble, and we have men and arms ready to assist y. Twenty-five men can be had at a minute's notice.' Murray says, 'If you want the men, say so.' I told him as long as they stayed at the O.K. Corral - where at this time they were - I would not go down to disarm them; that if they came on the street I would disarm them. He says, 'You can count on me if there is any danger.' I walked then from Hafford's across Fourth Street west. J.L. Fonck met me there and says, 'the cowboys are making threats against you, and if you want any help I can furnish ten men.' I told him I wouldn't bother them as long as they were in the corral; that if they showed up on the street I would disarm them. He replied, "They are all down there on Fremont Street now. Then I called on Morgan and Wyatt Earp and Doc Holliday, to help me disarm them."

Ike Clanton, the man who started the fight, then lost his nerve and refused to pull his gun, told his story of the gunfight:

"I, the McLaury brothers, and William Clanton and Billy Claiborne were standing talking in a vacant lot, west of the photograph gallery on Fremont Street, between that and the building next to it. The sheriff, Behan, came down and told us he had come to arrest and disarm us. I asked the sheriff what for. He told me to preserve the peace. I told him I had no arms. Then Wm. Clanton told him he was just leaving town. The sheriff then said if he was leaving town, all right. He then told Tom and Frank McLaury he would have to take their arms. Tom McLaury told him he had none. Frank McLaury said he would go out of town, but did not want to give his arms up until the parties that had hit his brother were disarmed. The sheriff told him he should do it and to take his arms up to his - the sheriffs - office and lay them off. Then Frank McLaury said he had business in town he would like to attend to, but he would not lay aside his arms and attend to his business unless the Earps were disarmed. The sheriff then put his arms around me and felt if I was armed. Tom McLaury said, 'I'm not armed either,' and opened his coat this way. (Witness throws back the lapels of his coat." (Tom was not wearing a coat. He was dressed in a dark blue blouse, dark pants and vest. The blouse came down outside his pants to the length of his arms.) "The

sheriff then looked up Fremont Street and ordered us to stay there until he came back.

The Earp party and Holliday just then appeared. Clanton and I remained because the sheriff ordered us to. Behan met the Earps, held up his hands and told him to stop, that he had our party in charge. The never stopped but passed by and came on where we were. It was about twenty paces from where we were they pulled their pistols and Wyatt and Virgil Earp said, 'You s—of ——, you have been looking for a fight,' and at the same time ordered us to throw up our hands. We threw up our hands and they commenced shooting. Morgan shot before Wyatt did. The first two shots were fired so close together I could not tell who fired first. Almost immediately after, perhaps a couple of seconds, Virgil Earp fired. Morgan Earp shot William Clanton. I don't know which of the McLaury boys Holiday shot at but one of them. I know Morgan Earp shot Billy Clanton because I saw his pistol pointed within two or three feet of his bosom and saw Billy stagger and fall against the house and put his hand on his breast where he was shot." (Had Billy been shot at this close range his clothes would have caught on fire.) "When Billy Clanton staggered and fell against the horse, he was holding his hands up level with the top of his head with the palms of his hands out. When those first shots were fired, Frank McLaury was holding his hands up level with the top of his head. I was holding my hands the same way. Tom McLaury threw open his coat by the lapels and said he had no arms. I was never armed at any time during the shooting. Morgan Earp had taken my arms a short time before that and left them behind the Grand Hotel bar. He took a Colt .45 pistol and a Winchester carbine.

When the Earp party came up where Billy Clanton and I were standing. Wyatt

Earp shoved his pistol up against my belly and told me throw up my hands and said, 'You s—of ——, you can have a fight.' I turned on my heel, taking hold of Wyatt and his pistol with my left hand and grabbing him around the shoulders with my right hand and held him for a few seconds. While I was holding him he shot. I pushed him around the corner of the photograph gallery. I went right on through the hall and out the back way. I went on across to Allen Street and seen no more of the fight."

(Ike saw very little of the fight, perhaps only the beginning. It has been established that he fled after the fourth shot. It is obvious that when he started running he did not stop until he was two blocks away. Unless he was running backwards, he could not have seen what was happening after the first four shots.)

Tombstone newspapers recorded the testimony of 26 witnesses in the weeks following the fight; twelve for the prosecution and fourteen for the defense. The Earp side of the story is best told by Wyatt Earp:

"When we turned the corner of Fourth and Fremont, we could see them. We had walked a few steps further when I saw Behan leave the party and come towards us; every few steps he would look back as if he apprehended danger. I heard Behan say to Virgil Earp, 'For God's sake, don't go down there or you will get murdered' Virgil Earp replied, 'I am going to disarm them— .' He, Virgil Earp, being in the lead When I and Morgan came up to Behan he said, 'I have disarmed them.' When he said this I took my pistol which I held in my hand under my coat and put it in my overcoat pocket. Behan then passed up the street and we walked on down. We came up on them close - Frank McLaury, Tom McLaury, and Billy Clanton standing all in a row against the east side of the building on the opposite side of the vacant space west of Fly's photograph gallery and the next building west I saw that Billy Clanton and Frank McLaury and Tom McLaury had their hands by their sides, and Frank McLaury's and Billy Clanton's six shooters were in plain sight. Virgil said, Throw up your hands; I have come to disarm you.' Billy Clanton and Frank McLaury laid their hands on their six shooters. Virgil said, 'Hold, I don't mean that; I have come to disarm you. "

(When Virgil said, "Hold, I don't mean that," he was not talking to the Cowboys. It was meant for Doc Holliday and Morgan. It is likely that he heard Doc cock that shotgun).

"They - Billy Clanton and Frank McLaury - commenced to draw their pistols; at the same time Tom McLaury threw his hand to hip and jumped behind a horse. I had my pistol in my overcoat pocket where I had put it when Behan

told me he had disarmed the other party. When I saw Billy and Frank draw their pistols, I drew my pistol. Billy Clanton leveled his pistol at me, but I did not aim at him. I knew that Frank McLaury had the reputation of being a good shot and a dangerous man and I aimed at Frank McLaury. The two shots which were fired, were fired by Billy Clanton and myself; he shot at me and I shot at Frank McLaury. I do not know which shot was first; we fired almost together.

The fight then became general. After about four shots were fired, Ike Clanton ran up and grabbed my right arm. I could see no weapon in his hand and thought at the time he had none and I said to him, 'The fight has now commenced; go to shooting or get away;' at the same time I pushed him off with my left hand. He started and ran down the side of the building and disappeared between the lodging house and the photographic gallery. My first shot struck Frank McLaury in the belly. He staggered off on the sidewalk, but first fired one shot at me. When we told them to throw up their hands, Claibourne held up his left hand and then broke and ran. I never drew my pistol or made a motion to shoot until after Billy Clanton and Frank McLaury drew their pistols.

If Tom McLaury was unarmed I did not know it. I believe he was armed and that he fired two shots at our party before Holliday, who had the shotgun, fired at and killed him. If he was unarmed there was nothing in the circumstances, or in what had been communicated to me, or in his acts or threats that would have led me even to suspect his being unarmed. I never fired at Ike Clanton even after the shooting commenced because I thought he was unarmed / believed then and I believe now from the acts I have stated and the threats I have related and other threats communicated to me by different persons, as having been made by Tom McLaury, Frank McLaury, and Isaac Clanton, that these men last named had formed a conspiracy to murder my brothers, Morgan and Virgil, and Doc Holliday and myself. I believe I would have been legally and morally justifiable in shooting any of them on sight, but I did not do so or attempt to do so; I sought no advantage. When I went as deputy marshal to help disarm and arrest them, I went as part of my duty and under the direction of my brother, the marshal. I did not intend to fight unless it became necessary in self defense and in *the performance of official duty. When Billy Clanton and Frank McLaury drew their pistols I knew it was a fight for life and I drew and fired in defense of my own life, and the lives of my brothers and Doc Holliday."*

The most important witness was H.F. Sills, a Santa Fe railroad engineer. His testimony was of great importance because he was a total stranger in Tombstone, did not know any of the participants in the gun battle, and yet, was one of the eyewitnesses. He heard the Clantons and McLaurys threaten the Earps in the afternoon of October 26th. Since he did not know the Earps, he had someone point them out to him. His statement was:

"I saw the marshal and party go up and speak to this other party. I was not close enough to hear their conversation, but saw them pull out their revolvers immediately. The marshal had a cane in his right hand at the time. He throwed up his hand and spoke. I did not hear the word though. By that time Billy Clanton and Wyatt Earp had fired their guns off. The marshal then changed his cane from one hand to the other and pulled his revolver out. He seemed to be hurt at the time, and fell down. He got up immediately and went to shooting. The shooting became general, and I stepped back in the hallway alongside the court house. I afterward saw Billy Clanton, when he was dead, and recognized him as the one who had fired at the same time with Wyatt Earp."

Sill's unprejudiced statement verifies that Wyatt Earp and Billy Clanton fired the opening shots of the fight.

(Addie Bourland, who lived across Fremont Street from the O.K. Corral, was the best witness of all from her vantage point. First, she said Doc did not have a nickel-plated pistol, but a large bronze one. Actually, this was the shotgun. She also said that the Cowboys did not at any time throw up their hands!)

When all the testimony had been heard, Judge Wells Spicer rendered his decision. He took each question and considered it carefully. His words were:

"Considering all the testimony together, I am of the opinion that the weight of evidence sustains and corroborates the testimony of Wyatt and Virgil Earp that their demand

for surrender was met by Wm. Clanton and Frank McLaury drawing, or making motions to draw their pistols. Upon this hypothesis my duty is clear.

The defendants were officers charged with the duty of arresting and disarming brave and determined men who were experts in the use of fire arms, as quick as thought and certain as death, and who had previously declared their intention not to be arrested or disarmed.

In coming to this conclusion I give great weight to several particular circumstances connected with the affray. It is claimed by the prosecution that the deceased were shot while holding up their hands in obedience to the demand of the Chief of Police, and on the other hand the defense claims that William Clanton and Frank McLaury at once drew their pistols and began firing simultaneously with the defendants. Wm. Clanton was wounded on the wrist of the right hand on the first fire and thereafter used his pistol with his left. This wound is such as could not have been received with his hands thrown up, and the wound received by Thomas McLaury was such as could not have been received with his hands on his coat lapels These circumstances being indubitably facts, throw great doubt upon the correctness of statements of witnesses to the contrary.

The testimony of Isaac Clanton that this tragedy was the result of a scheme on the part of the Earps to assassinate him, and thereby bury in oblivion the confessions the Earps had made to him about 'piping' away the shipment of coin by Well's Fargo & Co., falls short of being a sound theory because of the great fact, most prominent in the matter, to wit that Isaac Clanton was not injured at all, and could have been killed first and easiest. If it was the object of the attack to kill him, he would have been the first to fall; but as it was, he was known or believed to be unarmed, and was suffered, and, so Wyatt Earp testified, to go away and was not harmed.

In view of the past history of the county and the generally believed existence at this time of desperate, reckless and lawless men in our midst, banded together for mutual support, and living by felonious and predatory pursuits, regarding neither lives nor property in their career, and at this time for men to parade the streets armed with repeating rifles and six shooters and demand that the

Chief of Police of the city and his assistants should be disarmed is a proposition both monstrous and startling. This was said by one of the deceased only a few minutes before the arrival of the Earps.

Another fact that rises up preeminent in the consideration of this affair, is the leading fact that the deceased from the very first inception of the encounter were standing their ground and fighting back, giving and taking death with unflinching bravery. It does not appear to have been a wanton slaughter of unresisting and unarmed innocents, who were yielding graceful submission to the officers of the law, or surrendering to or fleeing from their assailants, but armed and defiant men, accepting the wager of battle and succumbing only in death.

The prosecution claim much upon the point that the Earp party acted with criminal haste; that they precipitated the triple homicide by a felonious anxiety and quickness to begin the tragedy; that they precipitated the killing with malice aforethought, with the felonious intent then and there to murder the deceased and that they made use of their official character as a pretext.

I cannot believe this theory and cannot resist firm conviction that the Earps acted wisely, discreetly and prudently to secure their own self preservation - they saw at once the dire necessity of giving the first shot to save themselves from death. They acted; their shots were effective, and this alone saved all the Earp party from being slain.

In view of all the facts and circumstances of the case; considering the threats made, the character and position of the parties, and the tragic results accomplished, in manner and form as they were, with all surrounding influences bearing upon the result of the affair, I cannot resist the confusion that the defendants were fully justified in committing these homicides; that it was a necessary act done in the discharge of official duty."

In conclusion, Judge Spicer ordered Wyatt Earp and Doc Holliday released from all charges. Legally freed, the Earps and Holliday still had Death as a companion each time they strode down a Tombstone street.

A news dispatch sent out of Tombstone on December 2,1881, stated:

"The cowboy faction accepts the verdict with bad grace and a smoldering fire exists which is liable to break forth at any moment. It is well known that several prominent residents of Tombstone have been marked for death by the rustlers."

(The fact that the Cowboys had two horses led some historians to believe that the Cowboys were leaving town as they later claimed. Not true; the two horses belonged to Frank McLaury and Billy Clanton, who had just arrived in town and had not stabled their horses yet. Ike Clanton and Tom McLaury had come into town the day before in a light wagon which was at the West End Corral.)

(Just following the gunfight, Sheriff Behan had the bad judgment to say, before several witnesses in the Virgil Earp home, "I WENT DOWN TO THE CORRAL TO DISARM THEM, AND THEY WOULD NOT. I THEN MET YOU [VIRGIL] AND YOUR PARTY AND SPOKE TO YOU. YOU DID NOT STOP. I HEARD YOU SAY, 'BOYS, THROW UP YOUR HANDS, I HAVE COME TO DISARM YOU.' WHEN ONE OF THE McLAURY BOYS [FRANK] SAID, 'WE WILL!' AND DREW HIS GUN AND THE SHOOTING COMMENCED. I AM YOUR FRIEND, AND YOU DID PERFECTLY RIGHT."

This statement was made to Virgil before Deputy District Attorney W.S. Williams, Sherman McMasters, James Earp, Bessie Earp, Allie Earp, and Mattie Earp.

O.K. Corral

Owned by John Montgomery and Edward Monroe Benson was the scene of several violent deaths:

William Harrison Clanton	- shot -	1881
Robert Findley McLaury	- shot -	1881
Thomas Clark McLaury	- shot -	1881
Dr. George Willis	- shot -	1890
Jim Burnett	- shot -	1897

Chapter IX.

A LOGICAL LOOK AT THE GUNFIGHT

The newspaper stories of that day and time relate a fairly accurate picture of the gunfight. At the very least, they were statements of the time. Every individual who has ever heard of the Gunfight at O. K. Corral has a version of what caused it and of what took place that fateful day. Therefore let's look at some of the areas that are not often discussed.

First, regardless of movies, television, writers, and historians, the greatest, most famous gunfight of all time was never intended...it was an accident...a confrontation that got out of control. Neither side wanted or expected such a bloody spectacle.

There appear to be nine major causes that led to the confrontation.

First and foremost was the love triangle that had been formed between Josephine Marcus, John Behan, and Wyatt Earp. Josie had been living with Behan and Wyatt had brought Celia Ann Blaylock to town with him as his wife and was currently living with her. But when the two of them took one look at each other Josie moved out of the house with Behan and Wyatt moved away from Celia Ann and the two of them moved in together.

The second incident was the killing of Marshal Fred White by Curly Bill on October 27,1880. Curly Bill and his cowboy friends were handled rather roughly that night by the Earps and Doc Holliday and they never forgot it.

Politics was the third item that caused tremendous friction. Cochise County was to be formed early in 1881. All county positions were to be appointed until the general election. Behan, a Democrat, and Wyatt, a Republican, both wanted to be the first sheriff. Through an agreement between them Behan got the job, but did not live up to his political promises to Wyatt.

The fourth incident was the attempted stage holdup and murders of Budd Philpot, the driver, and Peter Roerig, a passenger, near Contention City on the night of March 15, 1881. The Earps captured one of the culprits, Luther King, and got him to reveal the names of the others involved. He was placed in Sheriff Behan's custody and was promptly allowed to escape.

An unusual deal was made between Wyatt and Ike Clanton. Well's Fargo offered a $3,600 reward, dead or alive, for the men who held up the Kinnear stage at Contention. Wyatt wanted to be elected sheriff next election, and he knew the capture of these outlaws would put him in office. So he proposed a deal whereby Ike and some chosen cohorts would put the outlaws into a position where Wyatt could capture or kill them. Wyatt would get the credit and Ike and his men would get the $3,600.

Word of this deal leaked out in Tombstone and this terrified Ike. He knew what his outlaw friends would do to him for double crossing them. The only solution he could see to get himself out of this predicament was to run the Earps out of town or get them killed.

To complicate matters, Behan and his cronies got Doc Holliday's girl friend, "Big Nose" Kate, drunk and convinced her to implicate Doc in the stage holdup and murders.

The fifth incident was the ambush and killing of "Old Man" Clanton, Charley Snow, "Dixie" Gray, Billy Lang, and Jim Crane in Guadalupe Canyon in August, 1881.

Many of the Cowboy gang, as well as several neutral citizens, felt that the Earps and Doc Holliday had a lot more to do with those deaths than they were saying.

A sixth incident was the robbery of the Bisbee stage on September 8, 1881. Frank Stilwell, a deputy sheriff of Behan's, and Pete Spencer were arrested by Wyatt, Morgan, Marshall Williams, and Billy Breakenridge soon after the holdup. It was yet another incident in the Earp-Cowboy feud which was rapidly approaching a climax.

The seventh incident was the Clantons and McLaurys began to threaten the lives of the Earps and Doc Holliday publicly in Tombstone. It is likely that they believed that the Earps would pack up and leave under the pressure of such threats. It is evident that they didn't know or understand the Earp boys.

Incident number eight occurred around noon on October 26th. Ike Clanton was on the street, armed with pistol and rifle, threatening to kill the Earps on sight. Virgil hit him over the head with his long barrel Colt and dragged him off to the judge, where he was fined and released.

Incident number nine occurred when Tom McLaury had the bad judgment to challenge Wyatt as they left the justice court. Wyatt invited him to make any move he wanted. When Tom hesitated Wyatt slapped him, then "buffaloed" him with his pistol and left him lying in the street.

Now that the incidents that caused the confrontation which evolved into the gunfight have been listed it is necessary that evidence be introduced to show that it was, indeed, an accident.

Wyatt, Morgan, and Virgil left Hafford's Saloon on the corner of Fourth and Allen Streets to go down to the O.K. Corral. Virgil, at least, went with the intentions of humiliating the Cowboys by pistol whipping and disarming them and running them out of town.

But, on Fourth Street, Fate intervened and added numerous pages to Tombstone's bloody history. Fate in the form of Doc Holliday, who caught the Earps in the street and insisted that he be allowed to go along.

O.K. Corral today

(Doug Clay photo)

Losers at the gunfight at O.K. Corral

(Jack Hellyer photo)

All things considered, it is apparent that neither side expected or was prepared for a gunfight.

First, an analysis of the Cowboys:

Where were there "big guns?" If they had planned or expected an all-out blazing gun battle with the Earps, surely they would have brought along such stalwarts as Ringo, Curly Bill, Phin Clanton, Frank Stilwell, Hank Swilling, and Pete Spencer, to name a few.

Where was Ike Clanton's gun? What kind of man would go to a gunfight without a gun, particularly a fight that he was largely responsible for precipitating?

If the Cowboys really intended to kill the Earps on sight, as they had publicly threatened, why didn't they take the readily available Winchesters and shoot them while they were out in the open on Fremont Street? Both the McLaury boys were well known for their skill with rifles and would have been quite successful in such a move.

And now, an examination of the Earps and Holliday:

If the Earps had really wanted to kill the Cowboys, why didn't Virgil shoot Ike when he found him over on Fourth Street threatening to shoot the Earps? Ike was armed (which was in violation of city law) and threatening Virgil's life. Virgil was the Town Marshal and a Deputy United States Marshal. If he had shot Ike dead under such circumstances no jury would have convicted him. But he didn't shoot him - just hit him over the head and took him to court.

And again, when Wyatt "buffaloed" Tom McLaury. Tom had challenged him - Wyatt could have shot him - but he didn't, although he would have been justified.

If the Earps had planned to eliminate the Cowboys, where were the rest of their big guns?... Sherman McMasters, Texas Jack Vermillion, Turkey Creek Jack Johnson, and Dan Tipton, gunmen all, and loyal Earp friends? (Warren Earp was recovering from a bullet wound at Adelia Earp's house in Colton.)

If the Earps really expected or intended gunplay why did Wyatt put his pistol back into his overcoat pocket when Sheriff Behan told him he had disarmed the Cowboys?

And, why was Virgil holding a cane in his right hand - his gun hand -when he told the Cowboys to throw up their hands? Before he could draw his pistol he had to first discard the cane. That is hardly the action of a man prepared and entering a gunfight where his very life depended on speed, skill and accuracy.

If the Earps intended gunplay, why did they walk up to within six feet of the Cowboys...far too close for a gunfight involving eight people with seven revolvers and double barrel shotgun? But, if they intended pistol whipping, one step and a 71/2 inch pistol barrel would have been just the right distance!

And why didn't Wyatt shoot Ike Clanton? Ike was foremost in position in the Cowboy faction and obviously the major cause of most of the trouble. But, Wyatt testified he let him go because he believed him to be unarmed.

Then the best reason of all: This famous gunfight took place in a vacant lot, fifteen feet wide, between two buildings. Why would nine supposedly sane men (Claibourne was still present) crowd themselves and two horses into such a small space - then start shooting at each other, particularly when one of them was a drunk carrying a double barrel shotgun?

And then there's C.S. Fly...that erstwhile photographer, who let his wife go hungry while he rode around the countryside taking pictures. A man who took pictures of his own studio while it was burning. But...took no photos of the Gunfight at O.K. Corral, which took place beside his studio and to which he was the second person to arrive on the scene.

It happened too fast? Perhaps...but how about the bodies and the location afterward: What about the "most impressive funeral Tombstone ever had?" Plenty of time was available for these. These actions did not resemble the C.S. Fly described earlier, did they?

Ike claimed to have been unarmed and did not produce a gun at the fight scene. Wyatt always said that Ike shot at the Earps from the safety of Fly's studio.

Wyatt and Virgil testified that they believed Tom McLaury had a pistol and fired two shots at the Earps. R. F. Coleman testified that Tom fired a pistol. John Behan testified that Tom was unarmed. After the hearing had been concluded and the verdict rendered, another eyewitness to the fight was found.

The Kansas City Star printed a story concerning a Mrs. J.C. Colyer, who had made a trip out west, and the story was reprinted in the Tombstone Epitaph, December 30,1881.

Mrs. Colyer had been visiting the home of her sister and brother-in-law at Boston Mill. She drove into Tombstone with her sister and stopped at the post office (now the Wagon Wheel Restaurant). Mrs. Colyer waited in the buggy and was an eye-witness to the Cowboy-Earp confrontation. An excerpt from her interview is : "They approached the Cowboys and told them to hold up their hands. The <u>COWBOYS OPENED FIRE ON THEM</u>, and you never saw such shooting. One of the Cowboys, after he had been shot three times, raised himself on his elbow and shot one of the officers and fell back dead. Another used his horse as a barricade and shot under his neck."

This seems to indicate that Tom McLaury did indeed have a gun and used it. Now what happened to that gun? It's likely that no one will ever know for sure. But, remember that the first witness on the scene was Johnny Behan and he went straight to Tom McLaury. He could have made that pistol disappear. It would have made the Earps look bad and that seems to have been Behan's ultimate aim in life.

(Other sources say that Wes Fuller, also one of the first ones there, picked it up and that Old Man Fuller (Wes' Father) had it around Tombstone for years.)

It was a gunfight in which everyone lost. The McLaury brothers and Billy Clanton died in flame and gunsmoke. Ike had to live with the fact that he ran away, leaving his brother and friends to be killed - until his own death - still a rustler to the end.

But what about the so-called winners? Doc Holliday was already in the grip of Death, which was soon to claim him. And the Earps - it was the end of their hopes for wealth and prestige as respectable businessmen in Tombstone. Two months later Virgil was shot from ambush and crippled for life. In less than five months, Morgan was shot from a dark alley and killed. Shortly after, Wyatt, one brother crippled, one brother dead - rode out, never to return.

A harsh fate, indeed, for eight men involved in an accident!

When the Earps and Holliday took that walk down to the lot next to Fly's some of them intended to disarm and arrest the Cowboys. Others thought this would be a good time to settle their problems. When would they ever get another face-to-face daylight opportunity with these people?

It is extremely doubtful if any of the Earp party expected such resistance from the Cowboys to being disarmed. Since Sheriff Behan had told them that he had disarmed the Cowboys, the Earp party had relaxed a bit, thinking that the worst was already over.

Once they had stepped into that 15 feet wide lot other things, unplanned and unexpected, began to happen. Doc Holliday realized full well why the Cowboys were on this particular lot. Ike was in an absolute rage because Doc had told him the night before that he had personally killed his old man and would relish doing the same to him. The window, which the Cowboys had gathered under, was the one to Doc Holliday's room. Ike had talked them into coming there to kill Holliday. Such a move would give them revenge for "Old Man" Clanton and would drastically lessen the fighting power of the Earp faction. Killing Holliday didn't seem like such a bad idea when they considered Doc against five of them. But, they hadn't expected him to bring the Earp boys home with him! And no one had said anything about Holliday having that shotgun!

Suddenly, it didn't seem like such a good idea anymore. Maybe they had better think it over!

Holliday, on the other hand, could see that they were on the verge of giving up. He couldn't allow that to happen! He had to provoke a fight. If they walked out of this lot without a fight he was a dead man. They would gang up on him sometime when the Earps were not around, or they would just murder him with a shot from the dark, as was their custom.

Holliday considered himself a dead man anyway, but he had no intentions of letting this bunch of rustlers do the job. So just as Virgil said, "I have come to disarm you!" Doc jabbed Frank McLaury with that shotgun and hissed, "We've come to kill you sons of bitches!" And they believed him.

Frank McLaury cried out, "We will!" and pulled his pistol. Wyatt, carefully watching for such a move, palmed his gun and shot him in the stomach. Wyatt knew that Frank was the logical one in the Cowboy faction to react to anything. Ike was all bluster and would do nothing but that, and Tom McLaury was slow to anger and, therefore, offered no threat the first two or three seconds. Billy Clanton was quick to anger but a slow thinker. Wyatt had to chose between Frank and Billy as the most dangerous, and he chose Frank. Billy did get off a quick shot and had it been accurate, he might have put Wyatt out of the fight.

Claims are made that Holliday got off the first shot and shot Frank McLaury. That is possible, but it does not seem logical to me. Doc had the shotgun in one hand and with that he could not have been the first to clear his pistol for action. Even if he had his pistol already in hand, his first reaction would be to fire the shotgun at Frank when he saw him pulling his weapon. He would have wanted to put Frank out of action and, then once that danger had been eliminated, he could then use the weapon he used best and which was the most familiar to him - the pistol. He did see Billy Clanton, with weapon already in hand, shoot at Wyatt. This was the next most immediate danger. Realizing that, and with Frank already hit hard, his first pistol shot was at Billy Clanton, scoring a hit.

As said earlier, Frank McLaury's first shot hit Virgil in the calf of the leg. Morgan shot Billy Clanton - his third wound.

Holliday shot Tom McLaury with the shotgun, then threw it down. Frank McLaury shot at Holliday, the bullet grazing his skin under his pistol.

Morgan and Doc shot at Frank - hitting him in the head - his second wound. It is difficult to tell which hit him, but Morgan seemed to be in the better position to have shot him.

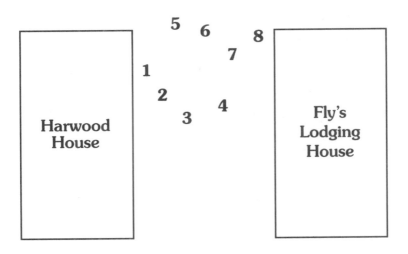

1. Frank McLaury
2. Billy Clanton
3. Thomas McLaury
4. Ike Clanton
5. Doc Holliday
6. Morgan Earp
7. Wyatt Earp
8. Virgil Earp

Several interesting items are noted:

Doc Holliday wore a gray suit and a long (ankle length) gray (Confederate gray) overcoat.

Wyatt, Virgil, and Morgan wore Navy blue or black midthigh Mackinaws. These are similar in color and make to a Navy pea-coat.

Billy Clanton had a Frontier Colt,1873, single-action, Army revolver, serial 52196, 44-40 caliber, 7-1/2 inch barrel, one piece walnut grips, blue steel; shipped from the factory to Simmon's Hardware Co., St. Louis, Missouri on July 19,1879.

Frank McLaury had the same type pistol, only with Serial 46338. His was shipped from the factory to J. P. Moore's Sons, New York, New York, on November 27,1878.

Tom had $2,923.45 in his pockets. (Even at $15 a head, that was approximately 200 head of cattle.)

On the subject of Tom and Ike being armed - they both, most likely were:

Tom, when the chips were down, pulled his and used it to help his brother and friends. After all the threats and humilia-tion from the physical violence it would have been ridiculous for Tom to leave his weapon at Mehan's Saloon a short time before the gunfight. If he did not replace the weapon at the gunshop, why did he replenish his ammunition?

Albert Billickie, owner of the Cosmopolitan Hotel, testified: "When he (Tom) went into the butcher shop, his right hand pants pocket was flat and appeared as if nothing was in it. When he came out, his pants pocket protruded, as if there was a revolver therein."

James Kehoe said that Tom was not armed while he was in Bauer's Market, but that he had "a long blue blouse outside of his pants."

Even Sheriff Behan testified: "Tom McLaury might have had a pistol and I not know it."

Virgil Earp said that Tom fired once, if not twice, from

behind his horse.

J.B.W. Gardiner said: "He (Tom) entered the butcher shop, and on coming out, I observed to one Albert Billickie that I saw no pistol but supposed at the time, on seeing the right hand pocket of his pants extending outwards, that he had gotten a pistol."

Wyatt Earp said: "If Tom McLaury was unarmed, I did not know it, I believe he was armed and fired two shots at our party before Holliday fired and killed him."

It seems totally illogical that Ike and Tom had been in town two days and had not checked their weapons. Virgil and Morgan took Ike's guns at about noon on the 26th, and Tom checked his rifle and pistol with Andy Mehan around 2:00 P.M. the same day. These men wanted the general public to know that were unarmed at the time.

Ike could never summon enough courage to pull his gun face to face with Earps and Holliday, so he fled with it still hidden.

Knowing that he had continually been demanding a showdown with the Earp faction, it would have been sheer folly on his part to go about amongst his enemies, the very ones he had been threatening, unarmed. His leaving his guns Grand Hotel bar (where Virgil deposited them) was a grand stand play for public eyes.

On October 29,1881, a special council meeting was called. The mayor said that the meeting was called to consider grave charges against Chief of Police Earp and it was ordered that, pending investigation of said charges, Chief Earp be temporarily suspended and James Flynn act as Chief during such suspension. (VIRGIL WAS <u>NEVER</u> PERMANENTLY REMOVED FROM OFFICE, ALTHOUGH HE DID NOT SERVE IN THAT CAPACITY AFTER THAT DATE.)

This is the telegraph sent to inform Will McLaury that his brothers had been killed. Sent from Tombstone on October 27, 1881 by L.H. Halstead.

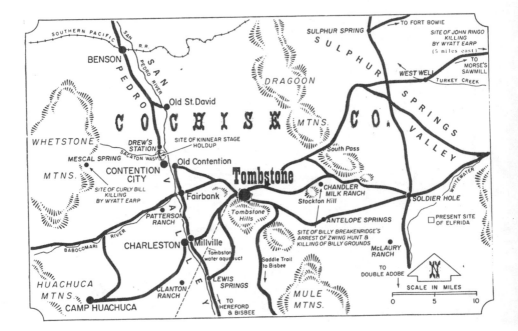

Chapter X.

RABBLE IN OUR CITY

On Saturday, October 29,1881, Ike Clanton filed a complaint, changing Wyatt, Virgil, and Morgan Earp, and J.H. Holliday with the murders of Billy Clanton, and the McLaury brothers. Sheriff John Behan served the warrants on Wyatt and Doc Holliday. Warrants were not served on Virgil or Morgan because they were still confined to their beds because of the wounds that they had received during the gunfight.

When Wyatt and Doc were taken before Justice Wells Spicer, they were denied bail, but when presented with affidavits showing the facts, bail was granted in the sum of $10,000 each being justified in the sum of $20,000 for each of the defendants. Bail was made immediately.

The Tombstone Epitaph, October 31,1881, printed:

"Today Holliday and Wyatt Earp were before Justice Spicer to answer to the charge. The investigation was conducted with closed doors. No one except the officers of the court, and the witnesses whose testimony was being taken, were allowed inside. The investigation is not yet concluded, and will probably occupy the court for several days."

Wells Spicer was a Justice of the Peace in Tombstone and, as such, had no jurisdiction to try a murder case. What the justice did was simply conduct a preliminary examination to determine if there was sufficient evidence on the charge of murder to hold the defendants for the Grand Jury.

There was such a protest from the newspapers and the gen-

W.R. McLaury

Brother to Frank and Tom who were killed in the gunfight.

Grave of Will McLaury in the
Synder Cemetery, Snyder, Oklahoma

(courtesy of J.A. Browning)

eral public that Spicer was forced to open up his courtroom. His hearing started on November 29,1881. During that time thirty witnesses testified.

William Rowland McLaury, an older brother of Tom and Frank, and a Fort Worth, Texas lawyer, arrived in Tombstone on November 4,1881. He requested, immediately, that he be allowed to assist the district attorney in the hearing. That permission was granted him. The very next day, November 5, he made a motion to put Doc and Wyatt back in jail and allow no bail. There was a great deal of argument between the attorneys, until, finally, Spicer granted the motion, Spicer ordered the sheriff to take them back into custody and detain them until otherwise notified.

Will McLaury was definitely determined to send the Earps and Holliday to the hangman for the deaths of his brothers. On November 8,1881, Will wrote a letter to his sister, Mrs. M.F. Applegate. In it he wrote, "the attorneys employed by me and the Dist. Atty. would not make the motion to have them remanded to jail." (EMPLOYED BY ME verifies that he was financing the prosecution of the Earps and Holliday).

Sixty-two leading citizens and firms of Dodge City sent an impressive testimonial as to Wyatt Earp's character. Signing it were county officers, city officials, judges, lawyers, clergymen, and citizens. It was notarized by the District Court Clerk. Of course, the prosecution (McLaury) objected strongly to its use in court, but Spicer allowed it anyway.

On November 19, the court had the Tombstone City Council Clerk, S.B. Chapin, read the city ordinances that showed that the Earp party had acted within the parameters of allowable legal action. Chapin read Number 7, Section 1, which stated that an officer could enter any place open to the public to arrest such persons engaged in causing breaches of the peace; and Ordinance Number 9, which prohibited concealed weapons and instructed that guns, dirks, and Bowie knives be deposited while an individual was in town.

Justice Spicer ended his hearing concerning the murder charges against the Earp party on November 29, 1881. Now Spicer had to determine whether or not his hearing had produced enough evidence to recommend that the defendants be held for the Grand Jury.

In voicing his opinion, the justice made much of the fact that the Cowboys had threatened the Earps and Holliday and had refused to relinquish their guns either to the sheriff or the town marshal until the lawmen were disarmed. Ike Clanton's claim that the gunfight was for the purpose of assassinating him did not sway Justice Spicer as his comment was that Ike was not injured in any manner while he could have been shot first and easiest had that been the purpose of the attack. Instead, he had been allowed to go away unharmed. He also said that for men to parade the streets armed with repeating rifles and six-shooters and demand that the Chief of Police of the city and his assistants should be disarmed is a proposition both monstrous and startling. (Epitaph, December 1, 1881.) With this clearly worded opinion he discharged the defendants:

> *"In view of all the facts and circumstances of the case; considering the threats made, the character and position of the parties, and the tragical results accomplished, in the manner and form as they were, with all the surrounding influences bearing upon the result of the affair. I cannot resist the conclusion that the defendants were fully justified in committing these homicides, that it was a necessary act done in the discharge of official duty."*

To a large number of people in Tombstone, the Spicer decision resulted in a renewed effort by the outlaws to retaliate. What the final result would be, no one knew for sure. On one side there were the courageous Earp brothers and the unpredictable Holliday. The other faction consisted of some of the most ruthless, cold-blooded killers of the outlaw minions in southeast Arizona. To many, the Gunfight at O.K. Corral was not the finish of the controversy, but just the beginning. History was to prove them right.

The Earps and Holliday, though legally freed, still had

Death as a companion every time they walked down a Tombstone street. A news dispatch from Tombstone on December 2,1881, stated:

"The Cowboy faction accepts the verdict with bad grace and a smoldering fire exists which is liable to break forth at any moment. It is well known that several prominent residents of Tombstone have been marked for death by the rustlers."

Those on that death list were Wyatt, Virgil, and Morgan Earp, Doc Holliday, John Clum, Wells Spicer, Marshall Williams, E.B. Gage, James Vizina, Tom Fitch, and a few others.

It is ironic that on November 28,1881, (the day before Justice Spicer concluded his hearing) Acting Governor John J. Gosper wrote a lengthy letter to U.S. Marshal Crawley Dake, concerning the multitude of problems in the Tombstone vicinity. Little did he know. He hadn't seen anything yet! Dake wrote a letter of explanation to the Acting U.S. Attorney General, F.S. Phillips, on December 3,1881. Excerpts from it deserve space here:

"I do not know of any rivalry between the U.S. officers and the county officials of Tombstone or elsewhere, that in any way, interferes or retards my deputies from bringing to Justice outlaws or 'cowboys' so called.

It is true that the Sheriff of Cochise County (bordering on Sonora), in which Tombstone is situated, attempted to interfere with the Messrs. Earp and their assistants but the attempt has completely failed. The Earps have rid Tombstone and neighborhood of the presence of this outlaw element. They killed several in Tombstone recently - and the sheriffs faction had my deputies arrested - and after a trial my deputies were vindicated and publicly complemented for their bravery and driving this outlaw element from this part of our territory. The magistrate discharged my deputies on the grounds that when they killed Clanton and the McLaurys they were in the legitimate discharge of duties as my officers. Hereafter, my deputies will not be interfered with in hunting down stage robbers, mail robbers, train robbers, cattle thieves, and all that class of murdering bandits on the border. I am proud to report that I have some of the best and bravest men in my employ in this hazardous business - men who are trusty and tried and who strike fear into the hearts of these outlaws. In conclusion, I beg leave to state that I am fully able to grapple with this outlaw element having this force of deputies at my command."

The Epitaph had long supported the Earp cause and the Cowboys knew it. Therefore, when the opportunity presented itself, they attempted to kill John Clum, Editor of the Epitaph and Tombstone Mayor. Clum had decided to go to the east to spend Christmas with his parents. On December 14, 1881, he took the stage from Tombstone to Benson, where he would make train connections. An Epitaph story shocked Tombstone the next day:

"HOLDUP!"

"As we go to press this morning we learn through the kindness of Mr. Samdom, one of Sandy Bob's drivers, that an attempt was made to stop the stage last night - about three and one half miles out of town. Simultaneously with the command to stop the coach came a volley of shots evidently aimed at the horses for the purpose of disabling them and thus stopping the coach."

"It could not be discovered in the darkness from whence the shots came or how many men were engaged in the assault. The horses were frightened at the firing and started off at a dead run, continuing their flight for about half a mile, when one of the lead horses fell dead, having been wounded by the highwaymen and the coach proceeded on without him. The robbers did not overtake the coach and nothing more was heard of them. The only casualties to the passengers was a slight wound on the leg received by 'Whistling Dick' and the disappearance of Mayor Clum, who was on his way to Tucson."

"As near as can be ascertained, Mr. Clum was on the outside and either fell or jumped off during the shooting. As nothing has been heard of him at present writing 2:30 A.M. - the gravest apprehensions are felt concerning his safety as unless he had been killed or wounded by the fusillade it would seem that he must have reported him-

self by this time... This information was obtained by Sandy Bob's driver when he met Kinnears coach on his way in last night. Arrangements are now being made to send out a party in quest of the missing mayor."

Clum showed up in Benson around 7:00 A.M. When the stagecoach caught up to "Whistling Dick's" wagon they realized that one of Dick's lead horses was shot. They cut the dead horse out and when the stage and wagon continued on toward Benson, Clum just stepped into the brush alongside the stage road. From there, he walked to the Grand Central Quartz Mill and borrowed a horse to ride to Benson."

(A gang of 20 men, including Ringo, Ike Clanton, Frank Stilwell, Curly Bill, Billy Claiborne, Hank Swilling, and Phin Clanton were the ones who attempted to murder Mayor Clum...and failed).

Justice Wells Spicer was also on the Cowboy's list. He received a letter containing a death threat:

"Editor Epitaph: -On Saturday morning I received the following spirited letter from the post office:"

"To Wells Spicer - Sir, if you will take my advice you will take your Departure for a more genial Climate as I don't think this One is Healthy for you much longer. As you are liable to get a hole through your coat at any moment. If such sons of Bitches as you Are allowed to dispense justice in the Territory, the Sooner you depart from us the better for yourself And the community at large, you may make light of this but it is only a matter of time you will get it sooner or later. So with these few gentle hints I will Conclude for the first and Last Time.

A Miner"

The Epitaph, December 18,1881, printed his reply. Excerpts of that reply are:

"There is a rabble in our city who would like to be thugs, if they had the courage would be proud to be called cowboys, if people would give them that distinction; but, as they can be neither, they do the best they can to show

how vile they are, and slander, abuse, and threaten every-
one they dare to. Of all such I say, that whenever they are
denouncing me they are lying from a low wicked and vil-
lainous heart; and that when they threaten me they are
low bred, arrant cowards, and know that 'fight is not my
racket' - if it was they would not dare to do it."

On December 16,1881, the Epitaph reported on Clum:

"MAYOR CLUM SAFE"

"The announcement in yesterday's Epitaph of the attack
upon the coach, night before last, threw the city into the
wildest excitement and the gravest apprehensions for
Mayor Clum. As before stated, upon receipt of the news
a party started out about 3:00 A.M. to obtain some tid-
ings of the missing mayor, among whom Sheriff Behan
and C.D. Reppy (Reppy was Clum's partner). The sheriff
and Mr. Reppy started first and arrived at Contention
between 4 and 5 o'clock where they learned from Mr.
Dunham, of Philadelphia, who was on the stage, the first
particulars of the affair. The six horse coach driven by
Jimmy Harrington and the bullion wagon driven by
'Whistling Dick' had just left Malcomb's water station,
which is the last house on the road to Contention, and
only about four miles from Tombstone and were bowling
along at a rapid gait when the order to 'halt' was given
from the roadside and almost simultaneously a volley
was fired into them. The off leader of the coach was
struck in the neck and all the horses became unmanage-
able. Dick was hit in the calf of the leg and received a
painful flesh wound, but , kept his seat and his wagon
right side up. The horses ran about half a mile when the
wounded one weakened and fell from loss of blood. Mr.
Clum, with the assistance of other passengers, cut the
leaders loose and on they went, it being the general
impression all the passengers were aboard. Mr. Clum had
been riding on the inside and he was missed but it was
supposed by his fellow passengers that he had taken a
seat on the outside, consequently his absence was not
detected until the arrival of the coach at Contention.

Upon learning this Messrs. Behan and Reppy started
from Tombstone and upon arriving at the place where the
attack was made examined the locality carefully but no
trace of the missing man could be found. In the mean-

*time the second party which had left Tombstone about
4:00 A.M., upon arriving at Malcolmb's station, learned
that two teamsters in the camp with their wagons at that
point had not only heard the noise of the shooting but
could distinctly see the flash, the attack having been
made at about the apex of the first rise beyond... The
party proceeded on to Contention where from Mr.
Dunham it was learned that, after assisting in the release
of the wounded leader, it was supposed by passengers
that Mr. Clum had either taken a seat with the driver or
on the bullion was on, while it was rationally presumed
by the driver that he was inside and his absence was not
ascertained until arrival at Contention. Just after leaving
Mr. Dunham, it was stated that Mr. Clum had been heard
of at the Grand Central Mill whither the party proceeded,
and learned that the mayor had taken the one road to the
mill, from whence, after resting he had gone by saddle to
Benson, arriving between 7 and 8 o'clock."*

The Daily Nugget, December 16,1881, carried an unusual
news item:

"A Close Call

A Little Difficulty in the Oriental Which Might

Have Ended in Bloodshed.

*An altercation occurred in the Oriental Saloon yesterday
morning which came very near resulting in the addition
of another chapter to the bloody annals of Tombstone.
Supervisor M.E. Joyce was in the place mentioned, conversing with Virgil Earp in regard to the attempted stage
robbery of the previous evening (attempt to assassinate
Clum). Joyce laughingly remarked to Earp that he had
been expecting something of the sort ever since they (the
Earps and Holliday) had been liberated from jail. Earp
became angry at the remark, and immediately struck
Joyce with his open hand in the face. The parties were
surrounded at the time by four or five of Earp's warmest
partisans, all heavily armed. Taking in the situation at a
glance Joyce, with rare good judgment and presence of
mind remarked, that a man would be a fool to make a
fight single handed against that crowd, and at the same
time commenced backing toward the door. As he reached
the door he said to the Earp party, "Your favorite method
is to shoot a man in the back, but if you must murder me*

*you will be compelled to shoot me in front," and thus say-
ing he stepped upon the sidewalk."*

It must be remembered that this was written by the Nugget,
no friend to the Earps. Neither was Milt Joyce. His statement
is absurd as there is no evidence that any Earp ever shot any
man in the back.

Following the attack upon John Clum, Acting Governor
Gosper made a second appeal to Washington and the
President sent his letter to Congress with a special message
whereby he requested that Congress amend the posse comita-
tus act so that he would be able to send military force into
Tombstone.

The Epitaph reported on this action:

"THE COWBOY CURSE

The Attention of Congress Called To It.

Special to the Epitaph:

*Washington, Feb. 9, (1992) - The President in a special
message to Congress, transmitted a communication from
Secretary Kirkwood, enclosing a letter from Acting
Governor Gosper of Arizona in relation to the prevalence
of lawlessness in that territory the President calls attention to the recommendation in his annual message that
the posse comitatus act be amended to permit the use of
the military in assisting the civil authorities to maintain
order, and suggests again such legislation as seems
required. In his communication Secretary Kirkwood
states that the New Mexico and Arizona difficulty in the
way arises from the fact that the sheriffs are intimidated;
that from personal motives they curry favor with the dis-
orderly element of society. It is therefore suggested
whether it would not be expedient and proper that
authority should be conferred by law upon the governor
of any territory to remove or suspend the sheriff for
neglect of duty and appoint a person in his place."*

The President's threats made no difference at all; the violence in Tombstone continued.

Alhambra Saloon

Shown here as the Owl Café and Tourist Hotel. In 1881 the building on the corner (southeast) of Fifth and Allen Streets was Jacobs Meyers Clothing store. The second building (left) was Tasker & Pridham General Merchandise. The structure upstairs (note arrow) was the Huachua Water Company office. It was still under construction when Virgil was shot from there on December 28, 1881.

Chapter XI.

SHOTS FROM THE DARK

The Cowboy faction had faced the Earps and Holliday in a gun battle once and had amply paid for their folly. They wanted no more of strategy that called for such a high price (3 dead). They had tried threats to no avail; and their murder plot directed at John Clum had failed. But, they had to do something about those Earps and soon. Desperate, they opted for another try at assassination. Their victim this time was Virgil Earp, deputy U.S. Marshal and suspended Town Marshal. The Epitaph, December 29,1881, describes the incident well:

"Midnight Assassins

U.S. Deputy Marshal Virgil W. Earp

Shot in the Back

The Facts as Far as Learned

About 11:30 o'clock last night, U.S. Deputy Marshal Virgil Earp was proceeding from the Oriental Saloon from the northeast corner of Allen and Fifth Streets to his room at the Cosmopolitan Hotel, and when he was about the middle of the crossing of Fifth Street five shots were fired in rapid succession by unknown men who were standing in the old Palace Saloon that is being rebuilt next door above Trasker and Pridham's store, on the southwest (southeast) corner of the same streets. (The remodeling was being done to make an office for the Huachuca Water Company.) Immediately after the firing the assassins ran rapidly down Fifth past the

Combination shaft and disappeared into the darkness beyond Tough Nut Street.

Two of the shots took effect on Mr. Earp, one badly shattering his left arm, and the other entering his left side, producing a wound the nature of which has not been ascertained at the present writing. Three of the shots went through one of the windows of the Eagle Brewery Saloon (Crystal Palace) on the northeast (northwest) corner in range with which Mr. Earp happened to beat the time of the firing. The holes in the windows were about at the height of four, six, and seven feet respectively above the sidewalk; but, fortunately, none of the inmates of the saloon were injured, the shots impinging harmlessly upon the opposite wall of the room.

Later Particulars

Since the above was written it has been learned that immediately after the shooting three men ran past the ice house on Tough Nut Street and sung out to the man in attendance who had his door open at the time. 'Lock your door.' The same three men were seen by a miner a few minutes later making down into the gulch below the Vizina hoisting works. The shots were evidently fired from double barrel shotguns, loaded with buckshot, and there must have been three men as five shots were fired in rapid succession. It is simply a miracle that Mr. Earp was not instantly killed, as in the darkness, with the simple aid of a bit of lighted paper the marks of nineteen shots were found on the east side of the Eagle Brewery and in the awning posts, three of them passing through a window on that side of the house.

Mr. Earp walked into the Oriental and told his brother Wyatt that he was shot. His friend escorted him to his room at the Cosmopolitan Hotel and Drs. Matthews and Goodfellow were immediately called in to attend upon him. It was learned before going to press that his left arm received the principal damage, the shot taking effect just above the elbow. So far as could be learned the wound in his back is not necessarily dangerous, though painful.

This further proves that there is a band of assassins in our midst, who, having threatened the lives Judge Spicer, Mayor Clum, Mr. Williams, the Earp brothers, and

Holliday, have attempted upon two occasions to carry their threats into execution, first upon Mayor Clum and second upon Virgil Earp. The question naturally arises, who will be the next subject? and a further question. How long will our people stand for this sort thing? It is no fault of these damned assassins that several persons were not killed in their dastardly attempt to murder a United States officer last night; for there were many people in the Eagle Brewery, over the heads of whom the passing shots flew on their course. A few inches lower and there would have been corpses prostrate upon the floor in place of frightened people wondering what had happened to cause this bombardment."

Virgil must have had a strong feeling of impending danger as on November 8, 1881, he had telegraphed General Orlando B. Willcox requesting military protection for his brothers and himself. Willcox would have been most happy to have granted his request, but the Posse Comitatus Act prevented him doing so. Evidently, he felt that Virgil was justified in his request as he referred it to Acting Governor John Gosper. Gosper disregarded the request because he knew that Tombstone had a Committee of Public Safety (Vigilantes) and Sheriff John Behan had notified him that all was quiet and peaceful.

The shotgun blasts did not knock Virgil down and when he turned to the source of the attack, he saw five men run; two in one direction and three in another. The night watchman at the ice house on Tough Nut Street said that he had seen Ike Clanton, Frank Stilwell, and Hank Swilling all run by carrying shotguns. A miner saw them run to their horses which were held by a man, who resembled Phin Clanton. (This horse holder was Pete Spencer. The two men who ran down Allen Street were Ringo and Johnny Barnes).

The wounds that Virgil received in his left arm and back were to cripple him for life. Surgeons removed four inches of shattered bone from Virgil's left elbow and twenty buckshot from his back and side. Virgil would have been killed by the ambushers had they positioned themselves a few feet closer, but it was plainly evident that they feared him and placed themselves too distant for the shot guns to be totally effective.

On December 29,1881, Wyatt Earp telegraphed U. S. Marshal Crawley Dake:

> *"Virgil Earp was shot by concealed assassins last night. The wound is considered fatal. Telegraph me appointment with power to appoint deputies Local authorities have done nothing. Lives of our citizens have been threatened."*

U.S. Marshal Crawley Dake immediately telegraphed to Tombstone Wyatt's appointment as Deputy U.S. Marshal on December 29,1881. Virgil Earp, lying on what everyone (even Dr. Goodfellow) believed was his deathbed, administered the oath of office to Wyatt.

Will McLaury was the mastermind behind the ambush of Virgil. He left town two days before it happened - but that was just an alibi for the time that the triggers were pulled. There can be little doubt but what he planned and financed the entire episode. The Tombstone Nugget, December 28,1881, read:

> *"W.R. McLaury, brother of the unfortunate boys killed not long since on our streets, left Monday for his home in Fort Worth, Texas. He will return in about one month for the purpose of settling up his deceased brother's estates/"*

A letter Will wrote to his father on April 13,1884, puts him in the proper slot:

> *"My experience out there (Tombstone) has been very unfortunate as to my health and injured me as to money matters, - and none of the results have been satisfactory.*
>
> *The only result is the death of Morgan and crippling of Virgil Earp and the death of McMasters."*

(Findley McLaury (Will's son) said that his father William Rowland, was taken by Ike Clanton. Before he left Tombstone to return to Fort Worth, he gave Ike one thousand dollars to follow Wyatt Earp and kill him. He said Ike took the money -

but hurried off in a different direction.)

The Tombstone municipal election was held on January 3, 1882. Sheriff Behan and the Nugget had high hopes of taking over the town. To make sure, Behan hired a hundred Cowboy sympathizers as deputies and instructed them to "keep order at the polls." The Citizen's Safety Committee had anticipated just such a move. Wherever a Cowboy took up his post, two well-armed committee members moved into position beside him. Neagle was elected Marshal and John Carr, Mayor, both by a landslide, indicating very little support for Sheriff Behan and the Cowboys.

The so-called confrontation between Ringo and the Earps and Holliday took place on January 17, 1882. Many "historians" like to say that Ringo challenged them all to do battle. Not so. Virgil and Morgan were still incapacitated from wounds received earlier. An article in the March 15, 1882, Epitaph noted:

> *"Mr. Virgil Earp was out upon the street this morning for the first time since he was hurt."*

Only Wyatt and Holliday are named as being present. Ringo wasn't running much of a risk as there was little chance they would accept his challenge. They knew he was drunk and besides, they already had enough trouble. Ringo was well aware of what he was doing!

What actually took place was an insignificant incident, best described by George Parsons in his journal:

> *"Much blood in the air this afternoon. Ringo and Doc Holliday came nearly having it with pistols. I passed both, not knowing blood was up. One with hand in breast pocket and the other probably ready, Earps just beyond. Crowded street, and looked like another battle. Police vigilant for once and both disarmed."*

The two antagonists were separated by Acting Town Marshal Jim Flynn, grabbing Ringo and holding him while Wyatt hustled Doc down the street. **THERE WAS NO ELABORATE HANDKERCHIEF DUEL!**

Wyatt, Doc and Ringo were arrested, as told in the Epitaph:

"Police Court: J.H. Holliday, Wyatt Earp, Ringo arrested for carrying concealed weapons. Earp discharged, Holliday and Ringo fined $30 each."

(Wyatt was discharged because he was a Deputy U.S. Marshal).

In late January, Acting Governor John Gosper and U.S. Marshal Crawley net with a few of Tombstone's leading citizens and during that meeting Wyatt Earp was given the status of a special officer with the power to deputize. He and his deputies were to serve warrants that had been issued by District court Judge William H. Stillwell.

While Marshal Dake was in Tombstone he was there to show support for the Earps. He also deposited $2,985 in the Hudson and Company Bank in an amount that would permit Wyatt to use it to outfit and maintain a posse. Wyatt only drew $536.35 of this money. Charlie Smith verified this as he was with him continually at the time. Smith said that Dake borrowed $100 from Wyatt during that time, too. Dake removed the rest of the account on February 7, 1882, for whatever reasons.

Parsons wrote in his journal on January 21,1882:

"Something brewing in town. Trouble ahead ."

On January 23,1882, Wyatt and his "federal posse" rode out of Tombstone. His posse consisted of Doc Holliday, Morgan and Warren Earp, Sherman McMasters, Dan Tipton, "Texas Jack" Vermillion, Charlie Smith and Turkey Creek" Jack Johnson. This posse carried warrants that had been issued for several of the Cowboys who were suspected of shooting Virgil. Ike, Phin Clanton, and Pony Diehl (a.k.a. Deal) were first on the list. Tombstone's new mayor, John Carr, issued a proclamation in the "Federal posse's" favor:

"To the Citizens of Tombstone:

I am informed by his honor, William H. Stillwell, Judge of the District Court of the First Judicial District that Wyatt Earp, who left this city yesterday with a posse, was entrusted with warrants for the arrest of diverse persons charged with criminal offenses, I request the public to abstain from any interference with the execution of said warrants. Dated: January 24, 1882

John Carr, Mayor"

J.H. Jackson

A second posse went out in search of the Cowboys, also armed with arrest warrants. The leader of this posse was J.H. Johnson and because he had no legal authority of any kind, his actions were destined to cloud the issues.

And, still a third posse went into the field to arrest some of the Cowboys. It is doubtful as to what this posse's objectives were, as it was lead by none other than Pete Spencer and Charles Bartholomew.

The Daily Nugget, January 31, 1882, reported:

"The Gentlemen Win

The Clanton brothers, Isaac and Phineas, for whom the United States Marshal's posse has been scouring the country for some time past, having repeatedly sent word that they were ready and willing to answer all charges against them and would surrender themselves to the authorities, if provided with the proper protection from the Earp posse, were on Sunday afforded that protection by a strong posse that went out under command of Charley Bartholomew and guidance of Pete Spencer."

"They Willingly Surrendered

themselves and arrived in town about 2:30 yesterday morning. They were in attendance at the opening of court to formally answer the charge against them. An order of adjournment of court was made by Judge Stilwell (Stillwell) that he might sit as an examining magistrate. Upon reading the complaint it was noted that they were not charged with robbing the mails as had been supposed, but they were accused of assault to commit murder, the specific offense being the waylaying and shooting of Virgil Earp some weeks ago. This warrant of arrest had

Virgil Walter Earp

After he was ambushed and crippled

(Glenn Boyer photo)

been placed in the hands of J.H. Jackson, who was not deputized either as deputy marshal or deputy sheriff, and consequently, it was held by the defense that he had no right to take or hold anyone in custody. Judge Alexander Campbell moved for the dismissal of the accused a motion ably supported both by himself and Ben Goodrich, Esq. The argument was taken down in short-hand, and tomorrow will appear in full, as some of the points were more clearly presented therein in regard to recent events than we could hope to do in any other manner. The motion was

Finally Withdrawn

Counsel stating that the defendants were willing to meet the allegations. His honor then remanded the Clantons to the custody of the sheriff pending the examination, or until bail was furnished in the sum of $1,500 each. The prosecution urged that the bonds be fixed at $5,000 each, but the court placed it at the amount mentioned above. Bondsmen were immediately procured and the examination was adjourned until this morning."

The Nugget continued the following day:

"Before Judge Stilwell (Stillwell) yesterday, sitting as an examining magistrate, the cases of Phineas Clanton and Pony Diehl were heard, the charges being assault with attempt to commit murder. No evidence being adduced to warrant their being held to answer, they were discharged from custody. The case of Isaac Clanton, on the same charge, was postponed until Thursday."

The outcome was as suspected. The Epitaph February 3, 1882, and the Daily Nugget February 4, 1882, reported:

The Clanton Trial

The trial of Ike Clanton and P. Clanton charged with the shooting of Virgil Earp, was held before Judge Stillwell last evening.

Dr. Geo. E. Goodfellow, the first witness, testified that on the night of the shooting he was sent for and dressed the wound. Witness testified also as to the nature of the wound.

Dr. Matthews testified to assisting in caring for the wounded man.

J.W. Bennett was called and stated that he had found a hat in the building - a new drug store - immediately after the shooting. The exit where the hat was discovered being about five feet four inches. Hat was produced in court.

Sherman McMasters was sworn and said that he was at Charleston on the night of the shooting, and that Clanton (Ike) was there. Witness asked Clanton about the shooting (of Virgil) at which Clanton replied that he "would have to go back and do the job over."

Messrs. McKelvey, Handy, Russell, Caldwell, Ayers, Clark, and Frost all testified that defendants were in Charleston at the time the marshal was shot, thereby provided an alibi."

"The Clantons and their friends took their departure from the city yesterday, having been honorably acquitted of the charges against them."

(Sherman McMasters had been a Well's Fargo undercover man, who had filtrated the Cowboy gang. He had actually ridden with them on occasions, but now he was openly siding with the Earps.)

Even though Justice Spicer had discharged the Earps and Holliday on November 29,1881, after a hearing on the deaths of the McLaury brothers and Billy Clanton, Ike filed murder charges against them again in Contention City on February 9, 1882.

The order for arrest called for any sheriff, constable, marshal, or policeman in the territory to take J. H. Holliday, Wyatt Earp, Morgan Earp, and Virgil Earp into custody. They were charged with the murders of William Clanton, Thomas McLaury, and Frank McLaury.

Any officer arresting the men named were directed to bring them to the office of Justice of the Peace, J. B. Smith on Main Street in the village of Contention. Sheriff Behan took the men named into custody with the exception of Virgil, who was still confined to bed from his serious injuries. The defendants filed a writ of habeas corpus petition on February 11,1882. In it they declared ; that Smith had no legal right to order their arrest. Further, the Grand Jury and Justice Spicer had already examined these same charges and dismissed them. Still, Judge J. H. Lucas ruled that Smith did have the authority to incarcerate them. Therefore, the Earps and Holliday would have to appear before Smith. On February 14,1882 Parsons recorded the following in his journal:

"Quite a posse went out. Many of Earp's friends, armed to the teeth. They came back later in the day, the good people below beseeching them to leave and try case here. A bad time is expected again in town at any time. Earps on one side of the street with their friends and Ike Clanton and Ringo with theirs on the other side, watching each other. Blood will surely come. Hope no innocents will be killed."

When Justice Smith saw the heavily armed men that were pouring into his court for the Earp and Holliday hearing, he didn't need anyone to advise him that the safest course of action was to adjourn the hearing to Tombstone. So, on February 15,1882, he again adjourned to a later date, showing that he was reluctant to conduct the hearing at all.

At this second postponement, the defendants filed a second writ of habeas corpus with Judge Lucas. That same day, Ike Clanton filed still another declaration against the Earps and Holliday in Judge Lucas' Court.

The judge was, by now, wishing that he had never heard of any of them. Lucas granted their writ of habeas corpus and ordered the defendants to be discharged from custody. Judge Lucas stated:

"Whether Petitioners are guilty or not, it is apparent to any reasonable being, that examination at this time would serve no good purpose. Unless new evidence or circumstances occur subsequent to the first examination, it would only duplicate the first hearing. "

On March 18,1882, the assassins struck at the Earp brothers once again. Morgan and Wyatt had attended the perfor-

Schieffelin Hall before restoration. Built as a dramatic shrine for the people of Tombstone by Al Schieffelin, brother to Ed, who discovered the town.

Schieffelin Hall 1995

The King Solomon Lodge No. 5 was chartered March 25, 1882, and started holding meetings upstairs. It still does. Morgan Earp attended a play here the night he was killed.

mance at Schieffelin Hall, then walked over to Campbell and Hatch's Saloon, between Fourth and Fifth Streets on Allen. Morgan was playing pool with Bob Hatch when a shot, fired from the darkness of the alley, struck him in the back. The bullet passed entirely through Morgan's body and lodged in the thigh of George Berry. (Berry did not die.) A second shot hit no one.

The Epitaph, March 20, 1882, read:

"The Deadly Bullet

The Assassin At Last Successful in His Devil Mission

Morgan Earp Shot Down and Killed While Playing Billiards

At 10:50 Saturday night while engaged in playing a game of billiards in Campbell and Hatch's billiard parlor, on Allen Street between Fourth and Fifth, Morgan Earp was shot through the body by and unknown assassin. At the time the shot was fired he was playing a game of billiards with Bob Hatch, one of the proprietors of the house and was standing with his back to the glass door in the rear of the room that opens out upon the alley that leads straight thru the block along the west side of A. D. Otis & Co.'s store to Fremont Street This door is the ordinary glass door with four panes in the top in place of panels. The two lower panes are painted, the upper ones being clear. Anyone standing outside can look over the painted glass and see anything going on in the room just as well as though standing in the open door. At the time the shot was fired the deceased most have been standing within ten feet of the door, and the assassin standing near enough to see his position, took aim for about the middle of his person, shooting through the upper portion of the whitened glass. The bullet entered the right side of the abdomen, passing through the spinal column, completely shattering it, emerging on the side, passing the length of the room and lodging in the thigh of Geo. A. B. Berry, who was standing by the stove, inflicting a painful flesh wound. Instantly after the first shot a second was fired through the top of the upper glass which passed across the room and lodged in the wall near the ceiling over the head of Wyatt Earp, who was sitting a spectator of the

Campbell & Hatch's Saloon & Billiard Parlor

Morgan Earp was shot and killed while playing pool with Bob Hatch at this table under the skylight. Shot came from the dark alley thru the door on left. The date was March 18, 1882.

game. Morgan fell instantly upon the first fire and lived only about an hour: His brother Wyatt, Tipton, and McMasters rushed to the side of the wounded man and tenderly picked him up and moved him some ten feet away near the door of the card room, where Drs. Matthews, Goodfellow, and Millar, who were called, examined him and, after a brief consultation, pronounced the wound mortal. He was then moved into the card room and placed on the lounge where in a few brief moments he breathed his last, surrounded by his brothers Wyatt, Virgil, James, and a few of his most intimate friends. Notwithstanding the intensity of his mortal agony, not a word of complaint escaped his lips and all that were heard except those whispered into the ears of his brother and known only to him were, "Don't, I can't stand it. This is the last game of pool I'll ever play." The first part of the sentence being wrung from him by an attempt to place him upon his feet.

His body was placed in a casket and sent to his parents at Colton, Cal., for burial, being guarded to Contention by his brothers and two or three of his most intimate friends. The funeral cortege started away from the Cosmopolitan Hotel about 12:30 yesterday with the fire bell tolling out its solemn peals of "Earth to earth, dust to dust."

Doctor Goodfellows' report on Morgan's wound was different from that in Epitaph. It said:

"He was in a state of collapse, resulting from a gunshot, or pistol wound, entering the body just to the left of the spinal column in the region of the left kidney emerging on the right side of the body in the region of the gall bladder. It certainly injured the great vessels of the body causing hemorrhage which undoubtedly causes death. It also injured the spinal column. It passed through the left kidney and also through the loin."

Morgan and Doc Holliday were of the same age and often gambled together in Benson, Willcox, Charleston, Galeyville, etc. Consequently, they had become good friends. When Doc was informed of Morgan's murder he went berserk vowing to personally kill all the men responsible. He went through the town kicking in doors, searching for those he suspected. Had he found them that night, there would have been several more bodies requiring the undertakers' attention.

Wyatt testified before the coroner's jury, but told them little. He had looked upon Virgil, shot to ribbons, and crippled for life. He had watched the men who had ambushed him go free, unpunished. He had held Morgan, his spine shattered by an assassin's bullet, in his arms while he died. He knew that law would do nothing to the ones who murdered Morgan. But he knew who they were, and that was more than enough!

Consumed with hatred and frustration, Wyatt knew a strong desire for revenge. Someone, had to pay for Virgil being crippled and Morgans death. Then Frank Stilwell boasted that he had fired the shot that had killed Morgan. He might as well have committed suicide. Either Wyatt Earp or Doc Holliday or both would certainly see that Morgan did not go unavenged for very long.

Morgan's body was embalmed, dressed in a blue suit, belonging to Doc Holliday, then laid out for viewing in the Cosmopolitan Hotel.

Wyatt and Warren Earp, Sherman McMasters, Turkey Creek Jackson , Doc Holliday, and several others escorted Morgan's body to Contention. Virgil would no longer be safe in Tombstone, crippled as he was. He would therefore be a hindrance to the job Wyatt had to do. So, Virgil, Allie, and Louisa went to Colton with Morgan's body.

The Tucson newspaper March 21,1882, said:

> *"Two of the Earp brothers and Doc Holliday arrived here last night from Tombstone. Virgil Earp passed on to Colton with the remains of his brother, Morgan, who was assassinated Saturday night at Tombstone. A body of 15 armed men accompanied the brothers from Tombstone to Contention and six on to this place."*

Marietta D. Spence also testified at the coroner's jury. She was the wife of Peter Spencer and she and her husband lived next door to Virgil Earp.

"Marietta D. Spence, being sworn, testifies as follows: Reside in Tombstone and the wife of Peter Spence; on last Saturday, the 18th of March, was in my home on Fremont Street; for two days my husband was not home, but in Charleston, but came home about 12 o'clock p. m. Saturday. He came with two parties one named Freis, a German; I don't know the others name but he lives in the house of Manuel Acusto. Then they entered the front room and began to converse with Frank Stilwell. When they had finished, Frank Stilwell went out and Spence went to bed. This all happened that night. Spence remained in bed until 9 o'clock a. m. Sunday. Freis slept there. The other man went to his house on Friday and stayed all day; went out Friday night but returned in a short time to sleep. Saturday he was out all day and up to 12 o'clock at night, when Spence came in. There was an Indian with Stilwell called Charley. He was armed with a pistol and carbine. He left Saturday morning with Stilwell and came back with him at 12 o'clock at night. Both Charley and Stilwell were armed with pistols and carbines when they returned to the house Saturday night. The conversation between Spence and Stilwell and the others was carried on in a low tone. They appeared to be talking some secret. When they came in I got out of bed to receive them and noticed they were excited, why I don't know. Stilwell came into the house about an hour before Spence and the other two· Stilwell brought me a dispatch from Spence saying he would be up from Charleston that night, Saturday; (received it about two o'clock in the day). Think Spence left last night, the 20th for Sonora. Don't know positively that he went. On Sunday morning Spence told me to get breakfast about six o'clock - which I did, after we had a quarrel during which he struck me and my mother during which he threatened to shoot me, when my mother told him he would have to shoot her too. His expression was that if I said a word about something I knew that he would kill me; that he was going to Sonora and would leave my dead body behind him. Spence didn't tell me so but I know he killed Morgan Earp; I think he did it because he arrived at the house all of a tremble, and both the others who came with him. Spence's teeth were chattering when he came in. I asked him if he wanted something to eat and he said he did not. Myself and mother heard the shots and it was a little after when Silwell and the other

(Courtesy of Talei Publishers

Pete Spencer

two men came. I think Spence and the other two men, although they might have arrived during the night, had left their horses outside of town, and after the shooting had gone and got them. I judged they had been doing wrong from the condition, white and trembling, in which they arrived. Spence and the two men had been for several days in the habit of leaving home in the middle of the day and returning in the middle of the night, but they never returned in the condition as they did on that night, and after hearing the next morning of Earp's death, I came to the conclusion that Spence and the others had done the deed.

Have not seen the Indian, Charley, since that night; do not know where he is. Four days ago while mother and myself were standing at Spence's house, talking with Spence and Indian, Morgan Earp passed by when Spence nudged the Indian and said "That's him; that's him." The Indian then started down the street so as to get ahead of him and get a good look at him. Freis is a German who works for Acusto as a teamster. Think he was with Spence, Saturday night and assisted in killing Earp, also Stilwell and Indian Charley.

Considering the times and conditions it certainly took a large amount of intestinal fortitude for Marietta to make that testimony. The author is surprised she survived.

Spence was a nickname. Pete Spencer was the name he went by, but his real name was E. L. Ferguson.

Freis, the German, was really named Frederick Bode.

The coroner's jury ruled that:

"Death was caused from the effect of a gunshot or pistol wound on the night of March 18, 1882, by Peter Spence (sic), Frank Stilwell, one John Doe Freis, and an Indian called Charlie, and another Indian, name unknown." (This was Hank Swilling).

The coroner's jury consisted of J. B. McGowan, Wm. Bourland, Thomas Sorin, E. D. Leigh, W. H. Ream, Robert Upton and P. L. Seamans. By the time that warrants were issued Frank Stilwell and Florentino Cruz were beyond any earthly law. But, as was to be expected, the Daily Nugget, August 4,1882, reported that the others were discharged on the grounds of insufficient evidence.

To settle the doubt in some minds, the Epitaph March 24,1882, stated:

> *"Mrs. James Earp (Bessie) and Mrs. Wyatt Earp (Mattie) left today for Colton, the residence of their husband's parents."*

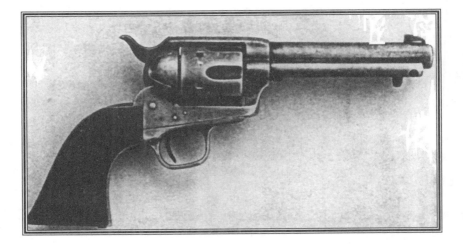

This Frontier Model Colt

Taken from Frank Stilwell's body. It is a .45 caliber single action serial number 1381. Quite likely it is the weapon that killed Morgan Earp.

(Courtesy Harry Stewart)

Chapter XII.

A BAD CHARACTER SENT TO HELL! and nine

As the Earp party put Virgil and the women on the westbound train they saw two figures bolt away into the gathering dusk. Wyatt jumped the tracks and chased a familiar figure - Frank Stilwell. Soon after a number of shots rang out and a shadowy figure crumpled onto the track bed cinders.

The Tombstone Daily Nugget, March 22, 1882, made this statement:

> *Tucson, March 21- This morning at daylight, the track man at the Southern Pacific Railroad depot found the body of Frank Stilwell about one hundred yards north of Porter's Hotel at the side of the track, riddled with bullets."*

When George Parsons heard about the demise of Frank Stilwell in the Tucson rail yard, he wrote in his journal, "a quick vengeance and a bad character sent to hell where he will be the chief attraction until a few more accompany him."

Excerpts from the newspapers of the day tell the details best:

Epitaph, March 22, 1882:

> *"The people of Tombstone were startled this morning with a report from Tucson that Frank Stilwell, a well know personage in this county as late deputy sheriff at Bisbee, and as one of the alleged Bisbee stage robbers, as also suspected of having killed an old man at the Brunckow mine some two or three years ago, had been found dead from the effects of a charge of buckshot, near the Porter House, at the depot in Tucson.*

As the dispatch says, there are two theories of the killing here as at Tucson. One is that the comrades of Stilwell, fearing that he might turn states evidence, have silenced him and the other, that it is the work of the incensed Earp brothers for the assassination of Morgan, it being stated that there is positive evidence that Stilwell was in Tombstone Saturday night at the time Morgan Earp was murdered; and that he rode into Tucson on horseback Sunday. In either case his taking off verifies the saying that, "the way of the transgressor is hard "

There is no doubt that Wyatt killed Stilwell. In an interview in the Denver Republican, May 14,1893, Wyatt told the reporter, "I went straight for Stilwell. He killed my brother. What a coward he was! He couldn't shoot when I came up to him, but just stood there, helpless and trembling. As I rushed to him he put out his hands and clutched at my shotgun. I let go both barrels, and he fell dead and mangled at my feet. I started for Ike Clanton then, but he disappeared behind a moving train of cars."

Tombstone Daily Nugget, March 22,1882:

"The assassination of Frank Stilwell in Tucson Monday night was, there is little doubt but another act in the bitter faction feud which has worked untold harm to the interests of Tombstone and Cochise County during the past six months. As all well informed persons were satisfied that the killing of Morgan Earp in this city Saturday night was the natural and legitimate sequence of preceding acts of violence, so, in regard to this latter assassination everybody conversant with the facts is equally well satisfied that it was but the natural outgrowth of the same causes. And as all right thinking and order-loving citizens denounced and deprecated the unlawful killing of Earp, so will the murder of Stilwell, which is surrounded by all the cowardly fiendishness of the former, create a feeling of loathing for the perpetrators and horror at the deed in the breasts of every man possessed of the common instincts of humanity or any regard for the preservation of organized society The Nugget condemned in words of no uncertain meaning the dastardly act of Saturday night, and it now denounces the red-handed assassins of Stilwell and places them in the same cate-

gory as the skulking murderers of Earp. It is to be earnestly hoped the cowardly perpetrators of two of the foulest, ghoul-like assassinations that ever disgraced any community, may be speedily identified, that justice, stern and unrelenting may be swiftly meted out to them."

Tombstone Daily Nugget, April 4,1882:

"The preliminary examination in the case of the Territory vs Pete Spence (sic), charged with the murder of Morgan Earp, was completed in the police court yesterday afternoon. The prosecution asked for Mrs. Spence (sic) as a witness the defense at first objecting. The prosecution then refused to proceed further with the case, whereupon the defense waived its objection. The prosecution, still refusing to proceed, the court ordered the discharge of the prisoner on the grounds of insufficient evidence. The testimony being the same in the case of Fritz (Frederick) Bode, held on the same charge; his discharge was also ordered "

Is it any wonder at all that Wyatt Earp ceased looking to the courts for any justice, and just took care of matters himself his own way? After the farce of trials on the crippling of Virgil and the murder of Morgan, it was plainly evident that the Cowboy faction had complete and absolute political immunity from any crime. Even the coroner s jury named Morgan's killers after just a few hours.

Arizona Daily Star, March 22,1882:

"Sheriff Behan yesterday received a telegram from the authorities at Tucson , requesting him to arrest Wyatt Earp, Doc Holliday, Sherman McMasters and one Johnson and hold them until further advice. Shortly after the receipt of the telegram, Sheriff Behan went to the Cosmopolitan Hotel, where he found the two Earp brothers, Wyatt and Warren, Holliday, Texas Jack, Johnson and McMasters. The sheriff informed the party of mission, when, in an instant each one leveled a six shooter at the officer, and peremptorily refused to submit to arrest. The sheriff retired, and immediately took measures to raise a posse to enable him to accomplish his duty.

Scores of volunteers proffered their services to aid in enforcement of the law, and arms for a sufficient number were quickly obtained from the store of P. W. Smith & Co. Immediately upon the enforced retirement of the sheriff from the hotel, the Earp party, six in number, also left the premises, all heavily armed, and betook themselves to the corner of Allen and Third streets, where their horses were, ready saddled, and quickly mounting, they rode rapidly out of town, in the direction of Contention. The sheriff, finding that the time consumed in arming and equipping his posse had enabled the other party to secure at least a half an hour's start, concluded not to commence the pursuit until this morning at 5 o'clock. "

Sheriff Behan was extremely careful never to catch up to the Earps and Holliday where he would be forced into a confrontation with an angry Wyatt Earp and a revenge-minded Doc Holliday. When he did blunder into their vicinity he quickly found his duties required his presence far away.

Arizona Daily Star, March 22, 1882:

"It is openly boasted by some that they will not deny the crime, and that their mission to our city was for no other purpose than to kill Ike Clanton, brother to William, who was recently assassinated in Tombstone by quasi-federal officials, and failing in their purpose, sought his next best friend and reeked the disappointed vengeance on him.

The boldness of the act, right at the depot in a peaceable city, around and amid the bustle of visitors at the train only adds to the offense, and effrontery of these desperadoes in transferring their enmity to those who were in our city under orders from the court, or had come here as a place of safety from these thirsty bloodhounds, is as provoking and outrageous to our citizens as it is damned in the sight of heaven.

It has been stated that Stillwell (sic), the unfortunate man, who fell victim, was a bad dangerous man. This may all be true. He has been twice or thrice arrested, once charged with murder, and once on suspicion of stage robbery, but in both cases the court, or examining magistrate pronounced him innocent. Let us give the man

*who is silenced in death by the assassin's bullet the ben-
efit of the courts' judgment. He cannot answer his
accusers now. Let his faults, no matter how grievous they
were, be interred with his body, for it must be remembered that those that slew him were his accusers in these
crimes. They failed to lock him in dungeon, but they did
not fail in his taking off.*

*But admitting that he was all that even his sworn ene-
mies alleged, that was no excuse for the crime. He was
not an outlaw. He was within the jurisdiction of the
courts and the officers of the law, and could have been
taken at anytime without the slightest resistance. The
presumption seems to be all in his favor.*

*In regard to the Earp party, no doubt but what they have
some warm friends who are good citizens. And undoubtedly it is this fact which has given them so long suffrage
in Tombstone. If one-twentieth part of what is said of
their record is true they are certainly no desirable acqui-
sition to any community They are a roving band; their
path is strewn with blood. Strange as it may seem, wherever they halt in a settlement stage robberies follow and
human life ceases to be sacred. Their late escapades at
Tombstone are only their records repeated in other frontier towns, and if we judge the honest sense of justice
and peace abiding disposition of our citizens, they will
never dare another such foul murder as was committed
last Monday night."*

This is a classic example of yellow journalism at its best.
The entire article is filled with outright lies and supposition.
The reason for slandering the Earps is because the Nugget and
the Star owners and editors were part and parcel of the political ring in the Territory. Therefore, they were compelled to present the news like they wished it was not the way it really was.

What they really didn't know was that Joseph Evans had,
early on, passed the information on to Wyatt that Stilwell,
Spencer, and a half-breed unknown to him (Apache Hank
Swilling) had been joined in Tucson by Ike Clanton.

Wyatt, while walking thru the railroad yard, passed a man,
who was dressed like a Mexican or Indian laborer. In the semi-

Frank Stilwell was killed near this building on March 20, 1882.

darkness Wyatt failed to recognize Hank Swilling. Had Earp found Clanton, Spencer, and Swilling that night there would have been dead bodies all over the rail yard. In that case the Nugget and the Star would have had some outstanding stories to write and could have been truthful in the telling. Just think of the hub bub created had Wyatt been able to bag all his four major enemies in one night!

The following document is the Stilwell inquest:

The evidence brought out before the Coroner's Jury -

The Verdict of the Jury

The following are the names of the witnesses examined and a synopsis of their testimony, and names of the coroner's jury before whom it was given, in the case of Frank Stilwell, who was killed near the depot a week since.

The jury were: L. D. Chillson, C. Rogers, W. A. McDermott, G. A. Clark , W. J. White and Lindsay. The names of witnesses and their testimony are given as reported.

Judge Murphy knew the body found near the depot to be that of Stilwell: was acquainted with him; saw him on Sunday and took a drink with him; believed his name to be Frank Stilwell.

Alman J. Hinckey was at the crossing near the depot when the train was near leaving; saw flashes of guns and some six or ten men standing on the south side of the track near where the body was found; did not see any arms with them nor where they went to; was with several others, all of whom were challenged; was about 7:15 p.m. when the shots were fired.

Dr. Dexter Lyford examined the dead body of Stilwell at the undertaker's establishment of E. J. Smith and found a single ball wound under the arm-pits, the ball having passed entirely through wounding the upper part of the lungs; also one rifle ball wound through the upper part of the left arm; also a charge of buckshot passing through the liver, abdomen, and stomach. This shot was fired very close, as the bullets were not scattered. Another charge of buckshot through the left leg fractured the former; also a rifle ball wound through the fleshy section of the right leg. Was confident that the immediate cause of death were the two shots - the one a rifle ball passing through the upper part of the body, and the other a load of buckshot passing through the stomach and liver. Either of the two shots were mortal and would cause death.

J.W. Evans was at the railroad depot when the train came in from the east. Saw Doc Holliday get off the cars, with a shotgun in each hand, a walk towards the railroad office. Shortly afterwards saw him returning without any guns. Heard him say to a small man who was standing near him to go and get the guns, pointing towards the office. Afterwards met Wyatt Earp at Porter's Hotel and while talking to him Virgil Earp came out of the hotel and shook hands with him. Wyatt Earp and lady then walked towards the back end of the sleeper and were assisted aboard the train by Virgil Earp and others who accompanied him. Then started up town, and shortly after leaving heard two shots immediately followed by four others. The engineer's bell rang and the train pulled out at about the same time. Returned and inquired the cause of the shooting, and was answered that it was done by some Mexicans below the depot. When he last saw the parties in question they had no guns with them. Saw Frank Stilwell at the depot when the train came in, and from the way his coat protruded thought he might have a pistol. Also saw Ike Clanton there.

David Gibson was at the depot with checks for passengers baggage. Met the train news boy who said "I guess there will be hell here tonight," and when asked why said, "the Earps and Holliday were aboard and were going to stop here as they had told him that the man who killed Morgan Earp was in Tucson." At this moment Doc Holliday, Wyatt Earp and another Earp and a short man walked from Porter's hotel towards the depot and appeared to be looking for someone. Holliday had an holster over his shoulder and a gun under it. The two Earps had short Well's Fargo's shotguns, believe that the short man had no gun so paid little attention to him as he was a stranger. As they reached the end of the sleeper one of them stepped on the platform and passed to the opposite side and then looked up and down the train, returning all four of them walked towards the rear end of the sleeper when they faced about and walked about towards the engine at the head of the train. The newsboy pointed out the wounded Earp who was sitting in the bar with two ladies in front of him. The conductor's bell then rang and two shots were fired towards the head of the train, instantly followed by about five more, could plainly see the flashes of the guns. but could not see, the Earps or the other man who he was informed by the newsboy, was McMasters.

W. J. Dougherty, lives within about 150 feet of where the body was found, heard one shot and saw the flash, then in about half a minute heard another followed in quick succession by two more and thinks he saw the upper part of a man's body; thinks that six shots were fired but saw nor heard anything to indicate that a man had been killed.

C. T. Brown, was going up Congress street toward the depot about five minutes after the train had gone out and just after passing the school house met four men dressed in dark clothes and carrying guns; they were going south towards Camp street. One man was also carrying an overcoat.

Nathan W. Waite resides at Ash Canyon in the Huachuca Mountains and came in on the same train with Virgil Earp and his wife, Warren Earp, Wyatt Earp, Doc Holliday and McMasters; joined them at Contention; McMasters said that they would leave the train at Benson but afterwards changed their minds and came to Tucson to see Virgil and his wife on their way to California. On the train McMasters particularly inquired as to the arrival and departure of trains at Tucson depot. All had guns and McMasters had two belts of cartridges.

E. L. Cohile - watchman at the depot, saw one man on the train with two rifles and am almost certain that he did not get off but went on with the train. He was about five feet eight inches in height, had on light coat, black hat and had dark whiskers.

Z. T. Vail - was conductor on the Western bound passenger train. When at Benson a lot of men got on the train, five or six of whom had guns. Two only had through tickets to Colton. They were Virgil Earp and wife. On arriving here one man with two guns followed me into the freight house and there left them, think that three of four had belts with cartridges.

Peter Dunphy - was at Dougherty's house about one hundred yards from where the shooting was, saw the smoke of the guns and heard five or six shots. The first of which sounded like a shot gun, the report being very heavy.

Isaac Clanton - was acquainted with the deceased whose name was Frank C. Stilwell and who was a native son of Texas, aged about 27 years. He told him I was expecting a Mr. McDowell from Charleston who had been summoned as a witness before the court in session here. Deceased had asked him to go with him to the depot. Went as far as Morgan's livery stable and then returned to town, the deceased continuing on to the depot. Afterwards went to the depot when the train from East was coming in and was on the hotel porch when rejoined by Stilwell, who called him to the rear of the hotel and told him the Earps and Holliday were aboard the train. After talking for a few minutes Holliday, McMasters, Johnson, Wyatt and Warren Earp came out of the hotel and walked towards the train. I then started towards my room, and the deceased walked down the track between the cars and the hotel. When below Morgan's livery stable, stopped for awhile, thinking that deceased would come up. In a few minutes heard the shots; returned to the stable and inquired about the shooting, but did not know Stilwell had been killed till this morning.

S. A. Batman was engineer on train when Stilwell was killed; saw a man with a Winchester rifle walking up and down by the side of the train and was told by someone that the man in question was one of the Earps guarding a party that were going through to California; shortly afterwards saw a man and lady come out of the hotel, the man carrying one arm in a sling; two men carrying Winchester rifles walked behind them. They got on the cars, the one outside still looking everywhere. Afterwards saw one of them walking down the track and in about five minutes heard two shots which were quickly followed by five or six others; heard some cheering in the direction in which the shots were fired.

John Hanlon: Left Tombstone on the 20th. Got on the train at Benson. When about half way between Tombstone and Contention, saw the Earp party. Some were on horseback and some were in a buggy. Also saw same party at Contention. There were Wyatt Earp, Warren Earp, Doc Holliday, McMasters, an unknown party and Virgil Earp and lady; all rifles and shotguns except Virgil Earp who had a pistol. McMasters is a small man.

Chas. Steward knew nothing whatever of the matter. A. McCann was at the depot when the train came in, saw four men with guns, also saw Virgil Earp and wife get into the car, also the three men who were with them, but they immediately came out and walked towards the head of the train; in a few moments heard six or eight or maybe ten shots, which were fired about the time the train started; also heard some cheering. The tallest man was one of the Earps, two of the men were short men, one was very short. Doc Holliday had a gun, saw him walk towards the new part of the hotel.

John E. Magee was at the depot on the evening in question; saw one of the Earps with a gun pass into the car for a moment then hurriedly return to the outside platform and look towards the engine, then stepping to the ground spoke low but excitedly to a stranger, they then passed forward towards the engine. Earp had a gun, a Winchester, but the other man did not. This occurred about five minutes before the train started. Immediately as the train left heard seven or eight shots in quick succession about 700 or 800 yards distant. James Kyle was at the depot but saw no man with arms, heard the shooting when near the school house of Congress street. Next morning saw a man lying dead near the track close to where there is a crossing. I. T. Marr is employed as a conductor, was at the depot on the night of the 20th, saw quite a crowd of men and heard that they were the Earp boys, saw one man with a gun, rang the train bell and about the same time heard shooting to the west of the hotel, was at the time in the sleeping car, saw one of the Earps in charge of his brother who had been killed, none of the crowd that seemed to be guarding Earp went off on the train.

James Miller; Fireman on west bound train on the evening of the 20th, saw a man running down the track on the east side of the engine and cross the track in front of it. Eight or ten minutes afterwards saw four armed men pass on the west side of the engine and down to the left of the coaches standing on the side track. In about five minutes afterward heard five or six shots fired in rapid succession. Saw but one man while they were shooting, but saw four men standing there when the train pulled out. Watched to see if the boarded the train. When they first passed down they all had guns; but when the train ran by a few minutes later the four men were standing where the firing had been done and had guns in their hands. Saw one man fire a gun. He was a middle sized man. The shooting was done by the same party who passed the engine. The man who ran down the east side and crossed the track had no gun. (This must have been Stilwell and he had his six-shooter.) Heard someone say before this took place that there would be murder done there.

R. E. Mellis: Was engineer on the outgoing train, and while on the lookout for tramps, saw a man cross in front of the engine, and shortly afterwards four armed men walked down on the west side of the train where the man was. Heard the fire. There must have been a dozen shots. This was in the neighborhood of the crossing. Pulled out so fast that they could not get on the train. They did not speak while passing. Did not see any gun in the hand of the man who ran across the tracks in front of the engine. Did not recognize him. Heard the firing and saw the flashes of the guns. Saw four men standing where the shooting had been done.

Brakeman Clark - came in with the party from Benson.

Engineer Clark was on the train when it was flagged and boarded at the Papago station going East.

This closed the evidence and the case was submitted to the jury who after consultation returned a verdict that the deceased was named Frank C. Stilwell aged 27 years, a native of Texas and that he came to his death at Tucson, Pima ' County, A. T., on the 20th of March 1882, 7:15 p. m. by gunshot wound inflicted by guns in the hands of Wyatt Earp, Warren Earp, Sherman McMasters, J. H. Holliday and Johnson whose first name is unknown, the persons by whose act the death of Frank C. Stilwell was occasioned.

What most of the news stories failed to report were items such as: Stilwell was a deputy sheriff when he robbed the stage; the driver positively identified him; his bootheels matched the prints left at the hold-up scene; neither was it mentioned that Sheriff Behan was his partner in the livery business.

Probably the best report written on the Stilwell killing was in the Tucson Weekly Citizen, March 26,1882:

"THE FATAL BULLET

A Sanguinary Affray at the depot.. Frank

Stilwell Dies With His Boots on...A Load of

Buckshot Through the Heart...The Sequel

to an Old Feud. Details of the Great Crime.

A young man by name of Frank Stilwell, aged about 26 years, suddenly terminated his somewhat erratic career a little west of the depot last Monday by death from gunshot wounds, by whom it is yet a mystery, and will be pending the report of the Coroner's jury, who are in session in the office of Judge Meyer. Circumstances point directly to the Earp crowd as being the real perpetrators. They were known to be on the outgoing western bound passenger train at the time of the shooting, which took place as the train was leaving the depot. The details of the crime are yet to be learned, but there are many who heard the shooting and some even saw the flash of the guns, but thought it to be no more than the reckless firing of some over jubilant citizen on account of the illumination. Daylight this morning however, revealed the dead body of Stilwell lying near the railroad crossing a short distance west of Porter's Hotel. It had evidently been robbed as the fragment of a watch chain was found attached to his vest, but the watch was gone, as was whatever else he may have had on his person. But the man evidently was not killed for his money, as the Earps are not commonly after that kind of game, and as it is well known that Stilwell belonged to the opposing faction, it is thought that out of revenge for the recent killing of their brother they, in truth, killed him. The body was brought to the morgue and stripped for inspection of his wounds by the jury, which showed how effectively he had been riddled. Death was evidently instantaneous although the expression of pain or fear on the face would seem to indicate that the man was aware of this danger, which he sought to avert with his left hand, as it was burnt and blackened with powder, that being the same charge which entered the breast as was evident from the close proximity of the gun when it was fired.

Frank Stilwell has of late years been known as a desperate character and for while was commissioned as deputy sheriff under Sheriff Behan of Cochise County but was removed because of a discrepancy in his accounts regarding the disposal of certain license money which had by him been collected He was afterward implicated in the brutal killing of old man Horton (van Houghton), whose brains were beaten out with rocks from some difficulty relating to the famous Brunckow mine lying south of Tombstone and which was at the time of the old man's death subject to relocation. Horton (sic) and others, among them Stilwell, were in the Brunckow neighborhood and intending to relocate on the following morning. Horton, most unfortunately for himself, was the successful one to the chagrin of Stilwell and gang, who determined upon his removal they effected by first shooting and afterwards brained the old man with rocks. A number of arrests were made, but because of some technicalities in the law, the implicated ones were liberated. Stilwell next came into notoriety on the robbing of the Bisbee stage which occurred in the early part of last October (sic) by the two masked men who not only stood demanded and received Wells Fargo's express box and the United States mail sack but also the passengers in line while they were most rudely searched and from one passenger, Mr. Ray, they obtained near $600, but their largest haul was from the express box which contained $2500. One of the robbers was or appeared to be of a jocese (sic) turn of mind and in the use of many cant phrases which were known to be familiar saying Stilwell he was pretty thoroughly assured and investigation by the proper officers convinced them that Stilwell was the one, if not the chief, actors in the robbery and he was accordingly arrested and underwent an examination in Tombstone, but again the uncertainty of evidence stood his friend as on the elicited facts it was impossible to convict him, but he was held to appear before U. S. Commissioner T. L. Stiles to answer for robbing of the mail, but on account of the killing of the Lowry (sic) in Tombstone, on whom he relied as witnesses he succeeded in getting bail, which he forfeited but afterwards, meeting with Judge Stile in Tombstone, expressed a wish to come back and stand his trial and it is supposed that such was his mission here at the present time as the indictment against him was still pending, but his death as stated settles all accounts. As his body lies in the morgue he has the appearance of a fine looking man being about 5 feet 10 inches high and would probably weigh 170 pounds. He is said to have come to Arizona from the Cherokee Nation and for awhile kept a corral and feed stable in or near Charleston and at which place he worked on a hay contract. He was buried this afternoon, the coffin being conveyed to the grave in an express wagon unfollowed by a single mourner."

South Pass

Pete Spencer's wood camp, where Florentino Cruz was killed, is on the other side of the pass.

Chapter XIII.

INDIAN CHARLIE and ten

While Sheriff Behan's posse was out chasing the Earp party in areas where they knew they would not encounter them, Wyatt had received information from friends that Pete Spencer was at his wood camp, which was located at South Pass in the southern portion of the Dragoon Mountains.

On March 22,1882, Wyatt and his "federal" posse rode to South Pass. But, Spencer was not there, fortunately for him. Instead, they found Florentino Cruz, whom Wyatt suspected had been posted on Allen Street as a lookout during the assassination of Morgan Earp. When the posse comprising Wyatt, his younger brother, Warren, Doc Holliday, Sherman McMasters, Turkey Creek Jack Johnson, and Texas Jack Vermillion came within sight of the camp, they saw Theodore D. Judah lying in the shade beneath a clump of trees. They rode straight for him. It was approaching noon.

Testimony of the witnesses before the coroner's jury follows:

Inquest held on Florentino

Samuel Williams being sworn says that he is a resident of Tombstone. On Wednesday the 22nd inst I was part of the time I was in Pete Spence's wood camp in Dragoon mts. part on road between there and town - part in town - left the camp as near as I can judge between 11 and 12 o'clock - I started out to hunt some mules that had strayed from camp. I supposed that they had came back to town - I did not find their trail in the neighborhood of a mile this side of the camp near some old houses. I heard shooting. I had been out of camp about half an hour or an hour at the time. The shooting seemed to me in the direction of our camp. I had in the meantime been hunting for the trail of the mules on both sides of the road backward and forward - when I heard the shooting I came direct to town and plenty quick - did not see anyone on horseback when I left camp - I saw one man - a woodchopper - only he was at work by the road - he did mention having seen anyone - I questioned him if he did so to inquire if they seen our mules - he was 300 or 400 yards from our camp - It was after this I heard shooting - I did not return to camp as I was afraid I might be killed by Indians, or someone else - I did not count but think there were between 7 and 10 shots - did not see Florentino after I left camp the shots were fired in quick succession - and I was satisfied the parties were shooting at somebody - there were four men in camp when I left - Judah, Florentino, Acosta, and another Mexican - the rapid firing caused me to think the parties were firing on someone and that someone was being killed. Did not know but it was Indians - also heard of the Earp party - and did not know but they might have came out that way - do not know any of the Earps men by sight. On Thursday the 18th I was in or about Tombstone. Did not see Florentino in town that day as I recollect - knew him by sight. On the day of the shooting I was armed with a six shooter - Have never had any difficulty with Florentino, or anyone else in the territory I left camp on horseback and struck immediately for the main road - did not at any time dismount until I reached town. Did not see anyone on a horse or mule after leaving camp. I know Pete Spence. He is a half brother of mine.

(Signed) S. R. Williams

Theodore D. Judah being sworn says he resides in Tombstone A. T. by occupation a teamster -

I know whose the body is which is now at the undertaking rooms of Ritter, the undertaker, and that was as / understand inspected by the Coroner's jury now present - I know him only as Florentino - last Wednesday we were all camped together, this Florentino, Sam Williams, and Ramon Acosta - two other Mexicans were camped in the

Immediate neighborhood. Do not know their names - about 11 or 12 o'clock Williams set out on horseback to hunt some animals that we had lost, and inside of an hour Florentino set out for the same purpose. He had not been gone more than half an hour - I was lying in the shade when I happened to look up, when I saw Wyatt Earp coming over the hill on horseback, and right behind him were several others riding in couples - six all togeth-er. Their names were Wyatt and Warren Earp, McMasters, Doc Holliday, Texas Jack, another party I do not know - I heard his name was Johnson - a large heavy set man - they came down to the camp of the two Mexican's fire - I heard them ask where does this road go to - heard no answer to this question - they stood talking among them-selves - they had not seen me until I called to them, and asked them if they had seen any mules this morning, and was answered by McMasters - He said he had seen some nearby and riding up to Wyatt Earp and spoke, the whole party immediately wheeled around and came in where I was - Wyatt Earp saw me, and asked me where Peter Spencer was - I told him I had left Spencer in town. He then asked me when I had left town - I said yesterday about 9 o`clock A.M. - As to the subsequent conversation I cannot recall it. He also I recollect asked after Hank, a half breed - I told him he was not there - he then asked me how many men we had out there. I told him exactly how many there were and what they were doing, and mentioned that there were two out in the hills hunting animals - He asked me what my name was, and a few more questions. One was when Spencer would be out to the camp again - He also made the remark, you are a friend of Pete Spence I believe, and Frank Stilwells too. I answered yes. He then turned and spoke to someone in his crowd, and asked them if they had seen any horses down there with saddles on - nothing more was said to me, and they went off passed out of my sight towards the main road leading towards Tombstone - I got up and went to the fire and was there but a few seconds - I spoke to Ramon Acosta and told him to come with me, and start-ed up the hill to see if I could get sight of the Earps - Had not gone 20 feet before I heard shooting - I turned to look to see if I could see where it came from, but could not see - I worked up the hill farther and saw the Earp party on top of a hill the other side of the road and I stood there watching them. They got off their horses on the hill and were there two or three minutes. they came down the hill again very leisurely onto the road and turned back towards my camp. They came a little ways and turned around again and went along the road until it makes a sharp turn, kept right on in the same direction easterly and disappeared in the hills. I and the Mexican then went back to the camp and worked there until evening taking one wagon up on top of the hill we left it there and went to where I thought the shooting had occurred. Ramon the Mexican maintained that Florentino had been killed.

We hunted around in the gulches and among the hills quite a while found nothing but the tracks of one horse and a man leading it. The tracks lead us to the road on the hill that goes up to the summit of the hill on which / had seen the Earp party. There we lost track of it amongst all the other trails. We then both went back to camp and stayed there all night.

Next morning I got my own team up to the top of the hill and decided to go and hunt that man again. I this time went clear up on the top of the hill to the spot where I saw the Earp party and looking around I discovered the body of Florentino. I stood there looking at him awhile and picked up his hat and went off. I went and unhitched my mules leaving the hat there at the wagon took one of the mules down to camp to get a saddle. On my way down I told Ramon of finding the body. I then proceeded into town here, for getting the hat. The body was lying at the same place where I saw the Earp party first after hearing the shooting. I had seen no other party or parties in the neighborhood during the day of the shooting. My camp is in the South Pass of the Dragoon Mountains. I accompanied that man who went out for the body under directions of the coroner. I did not see Williams again after he went out to the horses until I saw him again in town. He always went armed. I knew of no difficulty between Williams and Florentino. It was about 150 yards from the body of Florentino where I first struck the trail of the horse. I heard 10 or 12 shots. I worked about 3 hours and a half after the shooting before I began to search for the body. Mexican camp was about 50 yards from mine. Williams was armed and mounted when he left the camp and was armed with a 45 caliber pistol. The Mexicans went in the same direction that Williams went to look for the horses and I did not see Williams again. I think the Mexican (Florentino) was in town last Saturday night, and that Williams was not. Myself and two Mexicans were in camp when this party came there. Florentino and Williams were not. I am a very particular friend of Pete Spencers. Williams told me after I saw him in town that the reason he did not return to our camp was that he had heard the shooting and thinking it was done by Indians did not consider it safe to return and came in town. I know Ike, Phin Clanton and John Ringo saw neither of them out there that day. Ramon Acosta and myself were together all the time after this Earp party were in our camp - neither of us were in a position to see the shooting. The shots were one after the other in rapid succession - except the last which seemed to be held for 8, 9, or 10 seconds. Williams had been in our camp 3 weeks. Know that he was afraid of Indians - Know him as friend of Pete Spence and have heard that he was his brother. Heard no other shots that day than those I have referred to.

(Signed) T. D. Judah.

_____?_____ (Ramon) Acosta sworn says that he lives in Tombstone A. T. by occupation a laborer - on Wednesday last was out in the mountains in Pete Spence's camp - the man that was killed was in the same camp working with us - at about 12 o'clock he went out to hunt some mules that were lost - Just after he left 8 men arrived on horseback - out of the 8 men he knew two of them but not by name, Could recognize them if he saw them, one had a red mustache, the other a black, had seen them in town. When they arrived they asked me whose camp this was, they asked in Spanish. He said it was Peter Spence's camp. They talked among themselves, but as it was in English I could not understand except that I heard the name of Spence. They then left camp - Florentino was about 200 or 300 yards from where he was when he saw this party commence firing. When he immediately ran up the hill they were firing at Florentino. Did not see Florentino fall - but saw him going up the hill while they were firing and were following after. They stayed on top of the hill a little' while got down off their horses, walked around a little while then mounted and rode off. I know nothing farther - I started to hunt for Florentino, but did *not go far as I was afraid and returned to camp - am certain there were 8 men in the party - was not with Judah when he found the body - Judah was with me when I started out to hunt for Florentino the day of the shooting, but soon turned back. I was together with Judah when the shooting took p/ace. I know where they first found Florentino's body. I was down in the canyon and the other parties were up on the side of the hill when the shooting took place. Judah was with me at the time of the shooting. The party who did the firing were on horseback in pursuit of the man Florentino. The firing could be seen from our camp. The party who did the shooting were out of my sight one time until I ascended the hill. When I saw Florentino he was immediately in front of the parties who shot him.*

(his mark)

____?____(Ramon) X Acosta

Epiniania Vegas, sworn, says he resides in Tombstone A. T.

Last Wednesday was out in the (A) Pass of the mountains - Don't know the name of the pass in the Dragoons. I was on top of a little hill cutting wood -I heard a shot looked around and saw some men firing. There were 8 men doing the firing. I saw this man that was shot running and jumping from side to side. I saw him fall. They were about from 1000 to 2000 yards from me. After finishing the shooting they passed close to me on the main road - They saw me did not speak to me -I know the man that was shot. His name was Florentino. I do not know any of the party that did the shooting. I know Mr. Judah, at the time of the shooting Mr. Judah was in the canyon while 1 was on the hill. The party were Americans that did the firing - I heard 10 shots.

(his mark)

Epiniania X Vegas

Dr. Goodfellow, who examined the body of Florentino, the Mexican killed near Spence's (sic) camp last Wednesday, testified as follows:

"I am a resident of Tombstone; am a practicing physician and surgeon. I examined the body of the Mexican named Florentino at the undertaking rooms of A. J. Ritter and found four wounds on the body. I commenced the examination at his head and followed down. The first shot entered at the right temple, penetrating the brain; the second produced a slight flesh wound in the right shoulder; the third in the right shoulder, the third entered on the right side of the body near the liver and made its exit to the right of the spine, about five or six inches to the right. The fourth struck in the left thigh and made it's exit about seven or eight inches above the point of entry. In my opinion two of the wounds, those in the head and right side, were sufficient to cause death. The wound in the thigh was probably produced when he was lying on the ground after the wounds in the upper part of the body had been received. In my opinion the wound in the thigh was received after he was dead. I formed that opinion from the absence of blood around the wound " The Daily Nugget, March 25, 1882.

The report in the newspaper is more detailed than the jury's report. However, where the paper says the third wound was near the liver, the handwritten on-the-scene coroner's jury report says "region of the loin."

The half-breed Hank that Wyatt asked about was Hank Swilling.

Judah identified the six men who rode up to question him. Two other witnesses swear that there were eight men in the posse. There is no reason to suspect that they lied. The extra two were the ones who had been sent ahead to set up camp and then rejoined the posse between the time they talked to Judah and Florentino was shot.

The verdict of the coroner's jury was:

"We, the undersigned, a jury impaneled by the Coroner of Cochise County, Territory of Arizona to inquire whose body is that submitted to our inspection, when, whom, and by what means he came to his death, after viewing the body and hearing such testimony as has been brought before us, know that his name was Florentino Cruz, and that he came to his death from the effects of gunshot wounds inflicted by Wyatt Earp, Warren Earp, J. H. Holliday, Sherman McMasters, Texas Jack (Vermillion), (Turkey Creek Jack) Johnson, and two men whose names are unknown to the jury. (The latter two were Charlie Smith and Dan Tipton).

P. J. S. Tully	Webster Colby
M. Gray	C. H. Brickwedel
S. M. Barrow	Chas. B. Noe
John Kingsman	T. J. Blackwood
John M. Lee	M. H. Smith
A. C. Billicke	J. R. Adams

Over the years "sensation" writers have made the claim that Florentino was asleep with his right arm under his head and his coat covering his legs when the Earp posse came up on him. They shot him while he was sleeping, so goes the claim. Still other writers have Wyatt in a long conversation with Cruz, then giving him an advantage by counting to three, allowing Cruz to draw his gun on the count of one, while Wyatt would not pull his until the count of three. Such a variance of opinion emanates from those who are totally overcome by their own verbosity. None are true. These are the simple facts:

The Earp posse rode up on Florentino Cruz. There was no conversation.

He saw them.

They saw him.

He ran.

They chased him.

They shot him.

Nothing in the coroner's report, the testimonial record, or in the newspapers of the day indicate any explanation other than that.

No warrant was ever issued for the men who shot Cruz.

After all, Wyatt was a federal officer, and in such a capacity, could apprehend any of the people named by the coroner's jury as the murderers of Morgan Earp.

Florentino Cruz or Indian Charley was laid to his final rest in Tombstone's Boothill, having earned his niche in the bloody and violent history of "The Town Too Tough To Die".

Here's a Colt single action pistol once owned by Wyatt Earp. The pistol, (serial number 69562) was made in 1881 and had been in the collection of Capt. Fred W. Dodge, chief special officer for Wells Fargo & Co.

Cochise County Sheriff's badge

Back side of badge is inscribed: "John Behan 1881"

(courtesy Les Bugai, Jr.)

Chapter XIV.

AND HE HAS KILLED ME, TOO - eleven & twelve

When Charley Smith and Dan Tipton returned to Tombstone on March 23,1882, for supplies and information Sheriff Behan arrested them. He charged them with resisting arrest and obstructing justice in the arrest of the Earp party for the murder of Frank Stilwell "by use of threats, force, and the use of firearms."

Tombstone diarist, George W. Parsons, wrote in his journal,"...much excitement. False charges." When informed of Florentino's death he made this entry on March 23, 1882, "More killing by Earp party. Hope they'll keep it up. Paul (Pima County Sheriff Bob Paul) is here - but will not take a hand - If truth be known he would be glad to see the Earp party get away with all these murderous outfits."

The Daily Record of Sacramento, March 28,1882, confirmed what Parsons had written by this statement: "Sheriff Paul has returned from Tombstone. He says that he did not join in pursuit of the Earps because the posse selected by Sheriff Behan were mostly hostile to the Earps, and that a meeting meant blood without any probability of arrest."

Tipton and Smith were supposed to return to Wyatt Earp after a short trip into Tombstone to obtain money and supplies. Behan's arresting them spoiled this venture. Two other men, Dick Wright and Tony Craker were sent to meet Wyatt's posse in the Whetstone Mountains, carrying money.

Sharp criticism of Behan's tactics, coupled with the lack of solidity in his case against Smith and Tipton, brought an immediate outcry by Earp partisans and legal advocates in Tombstone that forced Behan to release the two men. However, he had detained them long enough to destroy their usefulness as couriers to the Earp party.

When Wyatt and his posse rode away from South Pass on March 22, 1882, leaving Florentino riddled with lead, he had a definite objective in mind. Earlier that morning he had received a report that Curly Bill and eight of his men had been seen in the vicinity of Iron Springs, which was about 30 miles northwest of Tombstone in a tiny valley at the edge of the Whetstone Mountains.

Curly Bill was a leader in the Cowboy gang and the man who had killed Marshal Fred White in October,1880.

Many people who knew Brocius well said that he was a wanted man from Texas. Curly Bill always claimed that his name was William Brocius and that he came from the Animas Valley in New Mexico.

All those claims aside, Glenn Mears tells a story told him by his Great Aunt Lizzie Brocius Chesterton: "Back in 1861 Curly Bill was just plain William Brocius, a poor dirt farmer just outside Crawfordsville, Indiana, with a wife and three children that he barely managed to feed. The children were named Jacob, Lizzie. and Ellie

Tired of the eternal struggle to master all his responsibilities, Brocius accepted $500 from a wealthy man, who had been drafted into the Union Army, to go to war in his place. After all, $500 was a fortune to a poor farmer back then. And so it was that Brocius went off to war, leaving his wife and three children to take care of the farm and themselves.

After the war ended in 1865, veterans began returning home - but not William Brocius. He still had not returned by 1868. His wife had received no word of him or from him. After so long, she believed that he was dead and married Charles Comer, a war veteran, in 1868. A child, named Jennie, was born to them in 1869.

Brocius showed up in Crawfordsville late that same year. As expected, he was extremely upset to find that his wife was married to another man and already the mother of the other man's child. He explained to his wife that he had been discharged in the deep South and without any money he had no other option but to work on farms along the way to raise enough funds to get home.

No one in the family believed this explanation. They believed that most likely he had been getting "rehabilitated" by living with some "southern belle." At the end of the war, many soldiers were given a small amount of money, discharged, and then had to make their own way back to their families. But in four years time Brocius could have crawled home!

He was angered by his family's attitude and soon left Crawfordsville. His family never saw him, or heard directly from him again. But they were to hear about him when he turned up in Arizona Territory in a town called Tombstone.

Along with Earp rode several gunmen. Doc Holliday, Turkey Creek Jack Johnson, Texas Jack Vermillion, and Sherman McMasters. Warren Earp missed the fight at Iron Springs because Wyatt left him at the road fork about five miles from the springs to meet Smith and Tipton. (He did not know that Behan had arrested them).

As they were riding alongside of a wash near Iron Springs, Wyatt was somewhat in the lead when nine men rose up from the wash guns spitting lead. "Curly Bill!" someone shouted! Brandishing a shotgun, Curly Bill was the front man. With the exception of Vermillion, whose horse was down Wyatt's posse fell back before the onslaught. Wyatt slid from his horse, unlimbering his shotgun. Scarcely had his feet touched the ground when he let loose both barrels point blank at Curly Bill. The twin charges of buckshot struck him in the chest, literally blowing him apart and hurling him against the opposite bank of the wash.

Glenn Boyer

At Iron Springs with a salute to the "wannabes" who would give their life to reach his status as an Earp historian - but they never will come close

WELLS FARGO SHOTGUN
USED BY
WYATT EARP
AT IRON SPRINGS ARIZONA MARCH 1882
STEVENS 10 GAUGE SHOTGUN #927

A photograph of the shotgun which, it has been claimed, was used by Wyatt Earp to kill Curley Bill Brocius. Author James E. Earle purchased the shotgun in September 1973 after making a special trip from Texas to Los Angeles where he made the bid for it during an auction. He calls it one of the last remaining links between two famous legends of the West — Tombstone and Wyatt Earp.

Casting the empty shotgun aside, Wyatt drew his rifle from his saddle, and using his plunging horse as a shield, continued the fight with the now leaderless outlaws. They had retreated, taking cover in the brush above the wash. Wyatt sprayed their brush cover with rifle fire. (Johnny Barnes was wounded in this gunfire). Since all the gunfire was directed at him, Wyatt tried to retreat. While riding toward Iron Springs he had loosened his gun belt several notches for comfort. When he slid from his horse it had slipped down, holding his legs together in such a manner that he was unable to mount his horse. Once he did manage to mount his horse he began a careful withdrawal before that murderous fire.

Wyatt retreated out of gun range and rejoined his companions. Vermillion exposed himself needlessly, trying to retrieve his saddle from his dead horse. None of the Earp party had been hit, but Vermillion's horse had been killed in the first fire. Doc Holliday had gone back to pick him up. Wyatt had several bullet holes thru his hat, coat, trousers legs, saddlehorn, and his bootheel, but suffered not a scratch on his person.

He was extremely angry at his friends because he felt that they had deserted him, leaving him in the face of the enemy alone. He never forgave them.

The group of ambushers had consisted of Curly Bill, Pony Diehl, Johnny Barnes, Hank Swilling, John Ringo, Milt Hicks, Rattlesnake Bill Johnson, Zwing Hunt, Billy Grounds, and Jim Hughes.

The entire population was divided on the question of whether or not Wyatt killed Curly Bill. Wyatt and the members of his posse maintained that he had blown Brocius apart. The Cowboys insisted that the outlaw was alive and well. The body disappeared, and the story leaked out that the Cowboys had buried it on Frank Patterson's ranch and concealed the grave.

The Tombstone Epitaph, run by John Clum, was a staunch supporter of the Earps and as to be expected, accepted the Earp posse's version of the killing of Brocius.

On the other side, the Tombstone Nugget, run by Behan's under-sheriff Harry Woods, naturally accepted the Cowboy version that Curly Bill was not dead. The Nugget offered a $1,000 reward to anyone that could produce Curly 's dead body. The Epitaph countered that by offering a $2,000 reward to any acceptable charity in the name of anyone who could produce the outlaw alive.

Many legendary tales abound concerning the sudden disappearance of Curly Bill Brocius, that he rode down into Mexico, married a Mexican woman and raised a hacienda full of kids; that he rode up to Wyoming to start over again; that he went to Texas and lived a peaceful life; and numerous other versions.

It is not logical that Curly Bill would vacate Arizona, just when everything was going his way. The Earps and Holliday were riding out, leaving him in complete control of southeast Arizona with no enemies to hinder him. There is no way he would not take one last swipe at Earp and the Epitaph by making them pay the $2,000 reward by showing up alive and well - if he were!

The two couriers, who replaced Smith and Tipton when Sheriff Behan arrested them, Dick Wright and Tony Cracker, arrived at Iron Springs after the fight was over, but the Cowboys were still there. The two couriers said they had two men wounded and one dead. They identified the dead man as Curly Bill Brocius, but did not know the wounded men.

Probably the most accurate telling of Curly Bill's fate can be obtained from letters written in the late 1920s by Fred J. Dodge, undercover man for Well's Fargo. Excerpts taken read:

"You will recollect that J.B. Ayers kept the saloon in Charlston that was the headquarters for all the outlaw and rustler element. This man, Ayers, for personal reasons that would take too long to tell supplied me with reliable information. Thru him I got in touch with several others. Johnny Barnes, who you will recollect was in the fight at Iron Springs, gave me much information, not only of that, but of many other things before he was killed. Afterwards, all that they said with reference to

Curly Bill was corroborated by Ike Clanton himself! It was my report to Mr. Valentine (head of Well's Fargo) with reference to Curley (sic) Bill that brought John Thacker out there."

"Referring to your letter of Sept.14, you ask for information about the death of Curley Bill. By reason of my connection with Well's Fargo and Co. and also because of my association with Wyatt Earp and others of his party, had full information concerning the fight at Iron Springs in which Wyatt Earp and party were ambushed by Curley Bill and party."

"Immediately after this fight I interested myself in ascertaining the true facts about the death of Curley Bill. J.B. Ayers, a saloonkeeper of Charleston, where the outlaws and rustlers headquartered, told me that the men who were in the fight told him that Wyatt Earp killed Curley Bill and that they took the body away that night and that they buried him on Patterson's ranch on the Babocomari. Johnny Barnes, who was in the fight and was badly wounded, and was one of the Curley Bill party, told me that they opened up on the Earp party just as Wyatt Earp swung off his horse to the ground and they thought they had hit Wyatt, but it was the horn of the saddle that was struck. That Wyatt Earp throwed (sic) down on Curley Bill right across his horse and killed him. That the Earp party made it so fast and hot that all of the Curley Bill party that could, got away. I made this report direct to John J. Valentine, President of Well's Fargo and Co. and in substance it was the same as the above. Mr. Valentine sent Thacker out there, and he, as you know, made a full investigation. Some time after this, Ike Clanton, himself, told me that Wyatt Earp killed Curley Bill."

"When John Thacker got to Tombstone, I got in his way so that he would come to me, and I personally gave him the names of the men to go to. They all talked to him, but Ike Clanton would have nothing to do with him, but he got all the information that he required and was thougherly (sic) and completely satisfyed (sic) beyond a doubt that Wyatt Earp had killed Curley Bill and that Bill was buried on the Patterson ranch."

"The night that Virgil was shot in Tombstone, Johnny Barnes was the man who fired the shot that tore up Virg's

arm I don't know who Wyatt attributed that shot to, but Johnny Barnes was the man. As I said, Johnny never recovered from his wounds, and finally died of them in Charleston where he was being cared for by Ayers."

Barnes said that on the night that Curly Bill was killed, that day he was put into a wagon, already containing the outlaw's body, and transported to Frank Patterson's ranch where the Cowboys gave him what medical attention they could. At the same time they buried Curly Bill somewhere near the barn and hid the grave. A few days later Barnes developed blood poisoning and had to be taken to J.B. Ayers' Saloon so that someone could care for him. As he lay dying in Ayers' back room he told Ayers a great deal of information. Ayers sent for Fred Dodge so that Barnes could tell him first hand.

Thus, Barnes told Dodge about burying Brocius at Patterson's ranch and knowing that his days were numbered he said, "Wyatt Earp killed Curly Bill and he has killed me, too." And he was right.

But, regardless of any information, facts, or otherwise, after the gunbattle at Iron Springs, Curly Bill went on no more cattle raids, hijacked no more smugglers, and was seen in his favorite hang outs no more. He vanished completely and was never seen again!

It was just like Doc Holliday, Wyatt Earp and Johnny Barnes told: Wyatt snuffed out Curly Bill's life with a twin blast from a double barrel shotgun. And he threw in Johnny Barnes for good measure!

The reason that Iron Springs was confused as Mescal Springs and Burleigh Springs is that John Clum did it purposely to prevent Behan knowing where the Earp posse was at any given time.

Following the fight at Iron Springs the Earp posse moved to pick up Warren Earp at the crossroads where they had left him. Then they went into camp about six miles north of Tombstone.

On March 25,1882, Charlie Smith and Dan Tipton were

released from charges by Sheriff Behan dismissed through the efforts of their lawyer, William Herring. Tipton stayed in Tombstone, but Smith joined the Earps in camp that night.

Parsons again showed his support for the Earps by the following:

> *"Sheriff Behan has turned all of the Cowboys loose against the Earps and with this lawless element is trying to do his worst... Feeling is growing here against the ring, Sheriff, etc., and it would not surprise me to know of a necktie party some fine morning. Things seem to be coming to this pass."*

On this same day, Hank Swilling appeared in Tucson to add his affidavit to Ike Clanton's murder charge against the Earps for killing Stilwell.

On March 26,1882, the Earp posse moved on to the McKittrick ranch. Here they had a meal then moved into camp a mile or so from the ranch house. Cochise County Deputy Sheriff Frank Hereford was at the ranch and when he saw the Earp party approaching he hid in an outbuilding.

On Monday afternoon, March 27,1882, the Earp party reached Hooker's ranch, which was known as the Sierra Bonita. It lay in the Sulphur Springs Valley between the Galiuro Mountains on the west and the Graham Mountains on the east; and about 22 miles north of Willcox.

When they rode into the ranch yard they were warmly greeted by Henry Clay Hooker, the Cattle King of Arizona. He was extremely happy to hear about the demise of Curly Bill. Hooker, close to the Cowboy haunts, had suffered from the Cowboy and Indian cattle thieves alike. He was a law and order man, who believed in being tough on any outlaw. A tough man, he was famous for his hospitality to visitors. Frequently, he remarked that he had "no use whatever for scrubs, man or beast."

Hooker happily provided food and drink for the men and their horses. Following a brief rest, the posse moved out about 7 o'clock that evening.

Behan and his posse of "brave, honest ranch men" arrived at Hooker's ranch about 7:00 A.M. the morning of March 28,1882. Not everyone agreed with Behan's description of his posse, which included Ike Clanton, John Ringo, Phin Clanton, Frank Patterson, Hank Swilling, John Lyle, Pony Diehl, Jim Hughes, Rattlesnake Bill Johnson, and a dozen or so of the lesser known Cowboys. This was the posse that Bob Paul refused to ride with.

The Tombstone Epitaph, April 14,1882, reported:

"The Sheriff and his posse rode up to the house of Mr. Hooker and DEMANDED refreshments for themselves and beasts which was freely granted them.

After Occurrences.

The following is a brief digest of the after occurrences at the ranch. Sheriff Behan asked Mr. Hooker if he knew the whereabouts of the Earp party. Mr. Hooker replied that he did not know and that if he did he would not tell him. Sheriff Behan then said, 'You must be holding murderers and outlaws then. Hooker said, No, Sir, I am not; I know the Earps and know you; and I know they always treated me like gentlemen, damn such vs, laws and damn you, and damn your posse, they are a set of horse thieves and outlaws.' At this, one of the honest farmers (?) of the posse spoke up and said, 'Damn the son of a b----, he knows where they are, and let us make him tell!"

At this Hooker's holster stepped away for a moment and returned with a Winchester, and drawing a bead on the 'honest granger said, 'You can't come here into a gentleman's yard and call him a son of a b----! Now you skin it back! Skin it back! If you are looking for a fight and come here to talk that way, you can get it before you find the Earps; you can get it right here!'

Mr. Hooker then turned to Sheriff Behan and said, 'These are a pretty set of fellows you have got with you; a set of horse thieves and cut throats!' Behan and Woods then spoke up and said, 'They are not our associates, they are only here on this occasion with us.' Hooker replied, "Well, if they are not your associates, I will set an extra table for you, and set them by themselves," which he did.

That Diamond Stud

After breakfast, Sheriff Behan went out to the stable and spoke to the hostler, sayng, 'Don't you say anything about this,' at the same time taking a diamond stud from his shirt bosom and presenting it to the holster, saying as he did so, 'Take this, it cost a hundred dollars, but don't say anything about what occurred here. 'He then turned to Mr. Hooker and remarked, 'If I can catch the Earp party it will help me at the next election.'

Leaving the ranch, they started off on the trail and crossed the valley to the foot of the mountains and then took up the valley and around to Fort Grant, where they tried to get Indian scouts. Behan offered $500 for the services of the scouts to Col. Bidwell, and during the negotiations, remarked that he wanted them to hunt down the Earp party, saying, I have just come from Hooker's ranch and I asked Mr. Hooker if he knew where the Earps were, and he said 'No, and I would not tell you if I did.' Col. Bidwell, stroking his beard with his right hand, looked straight at the sheriff and said, 'Hooker said he didn't know, and would not tell you if he did? Hooker said that, did he? Well, if he did.

YOU CAN'T GET ANY SCOUTS HERE!'

This ended the interview."

The Tombstone Daily Nugget, December 23,1881, told where Behan came by the diamond stud:

" Sheriff Behan was yesterday made the recipient of a beautiful and valuable present by his deputies. It consisted of two diamond studs and a handsome gold quartz scarf pin."

When Behan and his posse returned to Hooker's ranch, they told Hooker that the colonel wouldn't let them have any Indian scouts, even though they offered to pay handsomely.

Hooker laughed uproariously and said, *"You don't need any Indian scouts. Wyatt Earp and six other men are waiting for you over at that little hill."* (Reilly Hill).

The brave posse talked it over for a while, then decided that they had better get on back to Tombstone. Most likely, their 21 men compared to the 7 in the Earp posse didn't look like good odds.

Leaving the Fort Grant vicinity, the posse broke up, and Hank Swilling, Ike Clanton, and John Ringo headed into the Sulpher Springs Valley, riding at night. Pony Diehl met them and they decided that Arizona was not a safe place for them with that Earp party riding around God only knew where. They were left with little choice of where to go, so they rode south, and crossed the international border to Fronteras, Sonora, about 20 miles below the border. Feeling that they were safe from Wyatt Earp and his posse, they led a lazy life, drinking and gambling, until they ran short of cash.

Money was a must, so the four of them tried to hold up a trading post in Fronteras. When they burst in from the front with drawn-guns, they were totally and completely surprised to discover a dozen or more Rurales (Mexican police very tough hombres) gathered at the bar. Although they were surprised, too, the Rurales lost no time in opening fire on the American bandits. Hank Swilling was shot through the stomach - a fatal wound. His three friends left him and fled across the line into Arizona.

The three survivors would have been even more astounded had they known that Wyatt Earp was responsible for their almost fatal incident. Wyatt, Fred Dodge, and Bob Paul had long worked well with the lawmen, Emiliano Kosterlitsky and Captain Carrillo, below the border. Unknown to the general public, many exchanges of criminals had been done in the darkest hours of night. When the Mexicans pushed them across, the Americans would shoot or arrest them on American soil. And vice versa for the Mexicans.

What the four American outlaws had not known and probably never did, was that Wyatt had discovered where they were, mostly by the process of elimination. Kosterlitsky and his men were on their way to arrest the Americans and escort them back to the United States that night per the request of

Wyatt Earp. They had stopped for some refreshment, when they encountered the very men they were to arrest!

Wyatt didn't kill Hank Swilling - but his well-laid plans caused his demise. He was waiting near the border for the special delivery, but a twist of fate caused the attempted hold up and also caused the three that were fleeing for their lives to cross the border undetected by the Earp posse. Had Wyatt's plan been allowed to go as intended, he probably would have bagged all four of his deadliest enemies instead of Hank Swilling only.

Swilling was buried outside the parameters of the tiny local cemetery in an unmarked grave, without the benefit of a coffin or mourners.

As the people of Mexico say, "God will sort the souls."

The Arizona Daily Star, May 30, 1882, carried some interesting comments by Virgil Earp:

"The Cowboys

numbered at one time nearly 200 but during the last two years about 50 of them have been killed The most of them are what we call 'saddlers,' living almost wholly in the ` saddle and largely engaged in raiding into Sonora and adjacent country and stealing cattle which they sell in Tombstone. It is rarely that any of these stolen cattle are recovered. When the thieves are closely pursued and it seems likely that they will be overhauled, and the stock recovered, the Cowboys sell the cattle to some of the butchers practically in partnership with them, and I know of cases where the finest cattle in the country have been sold at a dollar a head. When cattle are not handy the Cowboys rob stages and engage in similar enterprises to raise money. As soon as they are in funds they ride into town, drink, gamble, and fight. They spend their money as free as water in the saloons, dancehalls, or faro banks, and this is one reason they have so many friends in town. All that large class of degraded characters who gather the crumbs of such carouses stand ready to assist them out of any trouble or into any paying rascality The saloons and gambling houses, into whose treasuries most of the money is ultimately turned, receive them cordially and must be called warm friends of the Cowboys. A good many of the merchants fear to express themselves against the criminal element because they want to keep the patronage of the Cowboys' friends, and the result is that when any conflict between the officers and cattle thieves or stage robbers occurs, followed up by shootings around town, as witnessed during the last few months, most of the expression opinion comes from the despera- do class and their friends, and the men who should speak loudest, and most decisively to correct the condition of affairs are generally the quietest. An officer doing his duty must rely almost entirely upon his own conscience for encouragement. The sympathy of the respectable por- tion of the community may be with him but it is not open- ly expressed.

The bad element knows its advantage in this respect, and makes the most of it. the Cowboys are collected from all parts of the western country, from which they have been crowded by advancing civilization, and they know that Arizona is about the only place left for them to operate in as an organization. With a complete breaking up of their company threatened in event of losing their hold where they are now, they resist official interference with the greatest desperation. Concerning the fights between the Cowboys and myself and my brothers, it has been stated over and over again that there was an old feud between us and some of our enemies, and that we were fighting only to revenge personal wrongs and gratify per- sonal hatred. All such statements are false. We went into Tombstone to do our duty as officers. To do that we were put in a conflict with a band of desperadoes, and it resolved itself into a question of which side could first drive the other out of the country, or kill them in it.

Chapter XV.

DESTRUCTION OF A LEGEND and thirteen

Many legendary tales have been told about John Ringo - few if any are true.

He was not a college graduate of William Jewell College - or any other such institute. (A letter from William Jewell College states that they have no evidence he ever attended there). His total education was grade school and much of that was received in Gallatin, Missouri, where his father operated a grocery store. This was during most of the War between the States so it is evident that the Ringos were not an aristocratic Southern family who lost everything in the war.

Young John did not return home from that conflict to discover the family plantation in ruins and head West to start over again. He was but eleven years old when the war began.

The Martin Ringo family did load up their meager belongings in May, 1864, and left Missouri with a wagon train that was bound for California. Their destination was San Jose where Mary Ringo's twin sister, Augusta, lived.

Augusta Peters Inskip Younger is the connection that started the fantasy that Ringo was related to the Younger boys who had caused so much trouble in Missouri and Kansas.

The real facts are that John's Aunt Augusta had married a Reverend Inskip, who had died, leaving her a widow. She then married a second husband, who was Colonel Coleman Younger, and he was an uncle to the infamous Younger boys.

So John was not a second cousin to the Youngers as many would have you believe. Truthfully, he was no blood relative of any sort. His Aunt Augusta had simply married into the Younger family.

The trip west was a horrible journey for the Ringo family. Constantly beset with Indian troubles as well a traveling problem, tragedy of the worst sort fell upon them at Deer Creek near Laramie, Wyoming. Martin's rifle accidentally discharged and the bullet struck him in the head disfiguring him horribly, but killing him instantly. Martin was buried quickly and his grave carefully hidden so that the Indians would not dig up the body.

Left with four small children and John, the oldest, only fourteen, Mary Ringo was not only grief stricken, but troubled as to what was to become of their little family.

They traveled on to Austin, Nevada arriving there October,1864. (This arrival time disputes the legend that John Ringo rode with General Joe Shelby in the battle of Westport, Missouri the latter part of October,1864. Not only was Ringo only 14 - but he was in Austin, Nevada at the time).

Disaster struck the Ringo's again after their arrival in Austin. Mary Ringo, who was carrying a child, had a miscarriage. It was caused by the hardships suffered and untimely death of her husband.

In order to obtain necessary funds the family had to sell most of their possessions which brought little under the circumstances. With these funds, Mary and all the children, except John, bought stage coach tickets to San Jose and continued their journey. John drove their wagon and team of mules the same route to San Jose.

When the family had arrived at Colonel Younger's they were given a small shack on the perimeter of the ranch to live in. Then, as far as the Colonel was concerned they were on their own.

Charley Ringo, a nephew of John's, reported that his uncle

was a teenage drunk and grade school dropout in 1869, when he left San Jose and went back to Indiana. From there he went to Missouri, then, eventually, appeared in Texas.

The fable makers say that Ringo was born in Texas. (He wasn't). They say that he carried books in his saddle bags. (He didn't - only whiskey). And that he read poetry and Latin around the campfire. (He didn't - he thought Latin was a Mexican). They also say that Ringo's brother was murdered by three men in a war between sheep and cattle men. (His only brother, Albert, died in San Jose of natural causes on August 29,1873). The fable continues that he tracked down the three murderers and killed them. Then he had to flee Texas to escape the law. The only correct part of this is the last sentence.

Ringo did become involved in the "Hoodoo War" in Texas - a range war between German families and American families. He joined Scott Cooley, who operated with the American faction.

On April 5,1875, Ringo was indicted by the Burnet County grand jury for "disturbance of the peace." The charges were that he had displayed a pistol in the public square.

On August 5,1875, when the case came up, Ringo failed to appear and the bond for $200 was forfeited. Sureties on the bond were M. B. Thomas and John W. Calvert. (Perhaps the word of John Ringo was as good as his bond).

John Ringo and another man rode up to James Chaney's house on September 25,1875 and killed him while his family looked on. Then they went into town and boasted of the murder publicly.

In November,1875, Ringo, Scott Cooley, and a group of men rode into Llano County, Texas to kill Peter Bader. They killed a man all right, but made a mistake and killed Charles Bader - not Peter, but his brother.

Ringo was indicted for his actions in the murder of James Chaney. He was released on bond in December,1877. The court dismissed the case for the reason "that testimony cannot now be procured to make out the case", in May, 1878.

When Ringo's family discovered that he was an outlaw and killer, they were embarrassed and ashamed and disowned him. In desperation, his sister, Mary Enna declared to everyone that her brother, John, was a Texas Ranger. (He wasn't!)

Ringo and his sisters were so at odds that when Mary Ringo died in 1876, he didn't even acknowledge that he had received the news.

The shooting of Lewis Hancock in Safford, Arizona on December 9,1879 , had been discussed early in this volume. However, the legend makers would have you believe that Ringo shot Hancock because he insulted a woman. In truth, it was a quarrel over nothing - instigated by a drunk Ringo! They would have you believe that Ringo killed Hancock. That isn't true either. Hancock recovered with only a scar to remind him.

Early in 1880, another unusual incident took place. Ringo shot another man. Yep, the "most feared gunfighter of all time" shot...himself. On March 3, 1880, Ringo wrote a letter to Pima County Sheriff Charles Shibbel explaining why he was unable to appear in court for shooting Hancock. He had shot himself in the foot and could not ride a horse!

Ringo was involved in another incident on January 14,1881. At the end of an all night poker game, John O'Rourke, known around all the local gambling dens as Johnny-Behind-the-Deuce, shot and killed W. P. Schneider, chief engineer of the Tombstone Mining and Miller Company. Ringo and several of the Cowboys were in the mob that seemed bent on lynching O'Rourke.

The lawmen conducted him safely to Tucson (still the county seat) where he was locked in jail. Two months later he escaped on the night of April 17, 1881. Sheriff Shibbel took his trail accompanied by three Papago Indian trackers. The Papagos struck to his trail like blood hounds though it veered around in circles all over town. They finally lost it at the south end of town near the Papago section. Johnny-Behind-the-

Deuce was never apprehended.

When the Kinnear Stage arrived at Drews station on the night of March 5,1881, a number of men (believed to be eight) attempted to hold it up. They were not successful, but Budd Philpot and Peter Roerig were killed in the attempt. Four of the killers were identified as Jim Crane, Luther King, Harry Head and Billy Leonard.

Wyatt Earp had made a deal with Ike Clanton to put the three remaining culprits (King had already escaped Behan's jail and disappeared) Head, Leonard, and Crane into a place where he could capture or kill them.

Before Ike and his henchmen could implement the plan, Head and Leonard got themselves killed over in New Mexico. The Epitaph, June 18,1881, tells the event:

"SENT TO MEET HIS GOD

How Bill Leonard Climbed the Golden Stair

A Pen Picture of a Desperate Affray

By An Eye Witness

A gentleman at Owl City, New Mexico, in a private letter to a friend in Tombstone, gives the particulars of the killing of Bill Leonard one of the Contention stage robbers, and mortal wounding of Harry, "the Kid; a cowboy of considerable notoriety The story is best told in the words of the correspondent, whose name we suppress for his own safety."

"THE NARRATIVE

Well about the shooting scrape: This place is their (the Cowboys) headquarters. Haslett and his brother Bill have a ranch in the Animas Valley, the best one in it, and old man Gray of Tombstone fame, has one on each side of it that he bought from Curley (sic) Bill and his gang and he wanted the one belonging to the Haslett boys, so some of the Cowboys were going to run the H. boys out of the country or kill them. On Friday last (June 10) Bill Leonard and three more Cowboys, as they call them, came to a store about one-quarter of a mile from the mine, that is owned by Parker, Joyce's partner in the

Oriental, and a man known as Baldwin. Well, the Rustlers went in there and got drunk and said they were coming up to the mine to kill the Haslett boys, so some fellow came up and told Ike, which put him on the look-out.

REVOLVERS AND RIFLES FOR DINNER

Yesterday, I went down to the store, getting there at noon, so I went in and ate my dinner. Bill Leonard and the others were at the table with their six shooters along-side their plates and their rifles lying in their laps, and a fellow outside guarding. I tell you it looked tough. Well, Bill said he was going to shoot the Hastell (sic) boys on sight, and we looked for them last night, but they did not come, so Ike thought that the best thing that he could do was to catch them himself, so this morning at daybreak he went to the store and laid in wait for them.

THE FIGHT

Back of the store is a corral and Ike and his brother got in there. The fence is about three-and-a-half feet high. Bill Leonard and the one they call Harry, 'the Kid'; (Harry Head) had to come down the road past the corral, so when they got within fifty yards, Ike and his brother Bill jumped up and opened fire on them. The Kid was on foot and Leonard on horseback. Ike let drive and got Leonard just below the heart, when he dropped to one side of his horse, when Bill thought that he would get away, so he plugged the horse and he fell. The Kid pulled his gun when Ike pulled on him and told him to stop, but he was going to pull when Bill Haslett gave it to him in the abdomen, and he started to run when both Bill and Ike commenced to pop it to him. They put six balls in him. When they picked Leonard up he breathed his last breath. Kid is still alive, but they think he will die soon. Bill Leonard said last night that he wished somebody would shoot him through the heart and put him out of his misery, as he had two big holes in his belly that he got the time tried to rob the stage at Tombstone. He was put out of sight (buried) at sundown this evening."

"The above letter was written Sunday evening June 12th. So it will be seen that Leonard has not been cold quite a week yet. The country is well rid of one of the worst des-

*peradoes that has cursed the world for a long time. In
this, as in nearly every similar case, can be seen the ful-
filling of the scripture saying 'He that lives by the sword,
shall die by the sword. "*

Not one of the residents of the Eureka Mining District condemned the actions of the Haslett brothers. A letter written by
Mrs. James Pender, wife of the superintendent of the Eureka
mines, revealed a great deal. An excerpt reads:

*"We have had lively times in camp this week. Had four
cowboys killed, and one of our own men by a bullet which
went through one of the other men. The first who were
killed were Bill Leonard and Harry Head, the two who
stopped the Contention stage some time ago near Drew
Station. The two who killed them were brothers, Ike and
Bill Haslett."*

The story of the outlaws' revenge on the Haslett brothers
was told by the Arizona Star, June 23,1881:

*"The killing of Bill Leonard and Harry, the Kid, at
Eureka, New Mexico by the Haslett brothers, has been
summarily avenged. It appears that a cowboy named
Crane organized and led a band of congenial spirits in
the work of vengeance. They followed the Haslett boys
for some twenty six miles from Eureka before overtaking
them and, as soon as they came up with them, the fight
to the death commenced. The Haslett boys were game
and made a brave fight killing two and wounding three of
the Crane party, but being over powered were finally
killed."*

The cowboy, named Crane, was Jim Crane, who was one of
the outlaws involved in the Contention stage holdup and double murder. He was also a crony of Ringo, Curly Bill, and Joe
Hill. Crane and these three were part of the "congenial spirits"
in these murders.

Another excerpt from Mrs. Pender's letter describes the
results:

*"Such nice fellows. I believe they had been cowboys, but
given up the business and abandoned that crowd and
were trying to reform. One was night engineer and the*

other worked in the mine. The innocent man who was shot, was the bucket man and was a quiet German. His given name was Joe. Don't know his last name.

My husband told me what he saw where they were killed. The place was just running with blood. Bill Haslett was shot six times in his bowels, and Ike twice through his stomach and once through his ankle. He suffered the worst of any of them. They were all conscious to the last."

The June 22,1881, Epitaph commented:

"On one point the country may be congratulated, and that is that two bold, bad desperadoes have paid the debt they owed an outraged community, whose presence they dangered and contaminated. "

The first of August, Ringo was with Curly Bill and the Cowboys, who ambushed the Mexican smugglers coming through Skeleton Canyon, killing nine of them and stealing $4,000 plus livestock and other goods.

It was but a few days later that Ringo again found himself in trouble - this time - robbery!

The Nugget, August 11,1881, notes:

'A SOCIAL GAME

Galeyville is noted as the rendezvous of the festive cowboy. It is there he must congregate and join in the amusements peculiar to the clan. On last Friday, one of them, known as Ringgold (sic) entered into a game of poker and not being an expert with the 'cards' as he is with his gun he went broke.

He returned with a companion named David Ester, who being good with a Henry rifle and the other with a six shooter. The players were promptly ordered to hold up their hands; and the cowboys proceeded to 'go through' the party, securing in the neighborhood of $500. Some of the party were so frightened that they broke to the woods where they remained concealed until daylight. A well known saloon keeper, who was in the room, had $500 on his person.

He dodged the Henry rifle and six shooter and escaped into the darkness, returning shortly with a shotgun, but the bold desperadoes had vamoosed. When the robbers left the town they took with them a horse belonging to one of the citizens."

Joe Hill was supposed to have returned the money and horse and explained that it was just a joke. Joke or not, Ringo was arrested and brought to trial. (During the course of this trial Ringo was to swear on two occasions that his true name was John Ringo, not John Ringgold).

When the Gunfight at O. K. Corral occurred on October 26,1881, Ringo was nowhere near. (It must be noted that Ringo managed to avoid a lot of the gun smoke business; Guadalupe Canyon; O. K. Corral; Tucson rail yard; Spencer's wood camp; Iron Springs; etc. He had no wish to face these people on anything like even terms.)

But, from the dark, he was long on courage. He was there when the Cowboys tried to assassinate John Clum on December 14,1881. Again, he was also present when they ambushed Virgil on December 28,1881. Ringo did summon enough "bottle courage" to challenge Doc Holliday on January 17, 1882. However, he was confident that Wyatt Earp would stop any action taken. He was also present when Morgan Earp was murdered on March 18,1882. He rode with John Behan's posse of "BRAVE, HONEST RANCH MEN," on the trail of the Earps and Holliday although they did not try too hard to catch them.

John Ringo, Hank Swilling, Ike Clanton, and Pony Diehl suddenly realized that their friends were dying and disappearing all around them. They could hear the message loud and clear "Those who had crippled Virgil and killed Morgan were dead men! It took no genius to see that the climate was safer and healthier below the border. Then when they tried to hold up a trading post and ran into a band of Rurales they deserted Hank Swilling, who had a bullet in his belly, and fled for Arizona.

Back in familiar haunts in Arizona, Ringo felt all alone. Phin and Ike Clanton had just moved north, up to Apache County, where their oldest sister, Mary Elsie lived. His enemies had all left the country, as had many of his friends, although many of the latter were dead. In a little over a year the list of cowboys, who had been eliminated, was astonishing: Old Man Clanton, Billy Clanton, Frank McLaury, Tom McLaury, Frank Stilwell, Florentino Cruz, Dixie Gray, Curly Bill, Johnny Barnes, Jim Crane, Harry Head, Bill Leonard, Luther King, Russian Bill, Charley Snow, Billy Lang, Zwing Hunt, Billy Grounds, Hank Swilling, and Frank Patterson,

Ringo was astounded that he found no one left to hate. He had been a drunk since his teen years and now he turned to the bottle; trying to solve his problems with whiskey, he went about for several days in a drunken stupor. Then, one morning, he saddled his horse and rode east from Tombstone.

Billy Breakenridge said he saw Ringo in the Dragoon Mountains, not far from Tombstone. He claimed to be the last man to see Ringo alive - but he wasn't, Ringo was drunk and still drinking. Breakenridge tried to persuade him to return to Tombstone, but Ringo was determined to go on to Galeyville.

Will Sanders saw Ringo later than that - drifting along near Lost Water on the Galeyville trail. Will spoke to him, but Ringo gave no answer. Sanders also said that he encountered Buckskin Frank Leslie, on the same trail a few miles behind Ringo. (Ringo had been drinking with Leslie and Billy Claibourne the past few days).

On July 14,1882, John Yoast, bound for Morse's sawmill, discovered a dead man in West Turkey Creek Canyon. The body was sitting in the intertwined limbs of oak trees. A bullet had entered the right temple and exploded through the top of the head.

The body was easily identified as that of John Ringo. Yoast quickly reported his grisly find to the sheriff. A coroner's jury was convened and they came to some hasty conclusions. (July is quite hot in Arizona and the body was already in deplorable condition). Although the statement of their findings did not say so, some of the jury called Ringo's death a suicide. (A close look at that jury shows that at least four of its members were either a part of the Cowboy clan or close associates). A few hours after the discovery of the body, it was buried near the trees and trail where it was found.

Strangely enough, no one, who lived in that vicinity, believed that Ringo committed suicide. Most of them did not agree on who killed him, but only that someone did.

When the body was found Ringo's horse, coat and boots were missing. The horse was found several days later in the Sulphur Springs Valley, about six miles from the body. The bridle hung from the saddle horn and the coat was tied behind the saddle. One boot was found near the horse, but the other was never found.

Another strange thing was that his undershirt bound around his feet was clean and dry. It had evidently not been walked upon. There had been a fairly heavy rain and only a few steps would have muddied the cloth.

The logical explanation is the Ringo's feet did hurt and he had removed his boots and hung them on his saddle. His camp was in the midst of large, granite rocks and they were quite hard on tender feet. Settling in for the night he used his undershirt to wrap and protect his feet. Walking on the rocks would not muddy the cloth. He would not walk very much on tender feet anyway.

The coroner's jury did nothing to clear up the mystery of Ringo's death. A great deal of controversy was created and still lasts until this very day. Down through the years historians, writers, and just curious people have presented numerous theories as to how Ringo died:

1. Ringo committed suicide:

    a. Because he was crazed by thirst. This theory is usually from those in the east who view Arizona as hot,

John Peters Ringo's grave in the Chiricahua Mountains. It is only a few feet away from Turkey Creek

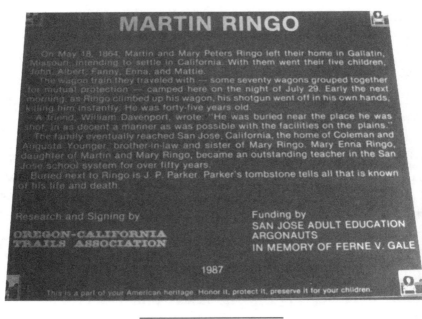

MARTIN RINGO

On May 18, 1864, Martin and Mary Peters Ringo left their home in Gallatin, Missouri, intending to settle in California. With them went their five children, John, Albert, Fanny, Enna, and Mattie.

The wagon train they traveled with — some seventy wagons grouped together for mutual protection — camped here on the night of July 29. Early the next morning, as Ringo climbed up his wagon, his shotgun went off in his own hands, killing him instantly. He was forty-five years old.

A friend, William Davenport, wrote: "He was buried near the place he was shot, in as decent a manner as was possible with the facilities on the plains."

The family eventually reached San Jose, California, the home of Coleman and Augusta Younger, brother-in-law and sister of Mary Ringo. Mary Enna Ringo, daughter of Martin and Mary Ringo, became an outstanding teacher in the San Jose school system for over fifty years.

Buried next to Ringo is J. P. Parker. Parker's tombstone tells all that is known of his life and death.

Research and Signing by

OREGON-CALIFORNIA TRAILS ASSOCIATION

Funding by
SAN JOSE ADULT EDUCATION
ARGONAUTS
IN MEMORY OF FERNE V. GALE

1987

This is a part of your American heritage. Honor it, protect it, preserve it for your children.

Martin Ringo's grave

Located about 2.7 miles west of the junction of U.S. 20 and state 95 Glenrock, Wyoming (courtesy J.A. Browning)

with rocks, sand, big cactus and no water. What they don't know is had Ringo fallen from where he was placed he would have fallen into Turkey Creek which has water year round.

b. He was bitten by a rattlesnake. There was no evidence to support this theory. Rarely was any adult local bitten by a snake.

c. His boots hurt. I'm sure they did. That's why he had them off. Remember that he had shot himself in the foot, but that was hardly a suicidal matter.

Two glaring facts totally eliminate the theory of suicide. One, there were no power burns. It is impossible to be shot at arm's length without leaving the burns. Two, he was found with pistol in hand, draped across his stomach. If the gun had been placed at his head when the gun fired, the recoil would have flung the arm out at full length, not across his body to the left. Remember also, that no one single person in the local area believed that Ringo committed suicide. even the coroner s jury later admitted that they did not believe it was suicide. It was just the quickest and easiest way to avoid a long, hot investigation with a body that was quickly becoming a problem.

2. Ringo was killed by Buckskin Frank Leslie:

Leslie had no motive for killing Ringo. Most of the time the two seemed to be on a friendly basis. Leslie was a Wells Fargo informer whom Fred Dodge paid well for useful information. Leslie became suspect because he was seen on the Galeyville trail, following Ringo. Leslie could well have been part of the conspiracy that did away with Ringo.

3. Ringo was killed by Johnny-Behind-the-Deuce:

Johnny killed W. P. Schneider, chief engineer at Charlston. Arrested, he was rushed to Tombstone for his own protection. Ringo was involved with the mob that tried to lynch him. Still in danger O'Rourke was moved to the Tombstone jail. He escaped from that jail on April

17,1881, and was never recaptured. The theory is that he came upon Ringo asleep and shot him in retaliation for trying to have him lynched. Those who believe this would have us think that O'Rourke hung around in the Chiricahuas with no money, no supplies, and a first degree murder charge over his head, and a fugitive from the law from April 17,1881, until July 12,1882. Then, at that time, found Ringo in that isolated area, shot him, then disappeared forever. The only truth in the preceding sentence is the last two words. When O'Rourke got clear of Tucson he was long gone - but spent the rest of his life looking back over his shoulder.

4. Wyatt Earp killed Ringo:

Josie Earp states in "I Married Wyatt Earp" by Glenn Boyer that Wyatt set up a rendezvous at Hooker's Sierra Bonita Ranch near Fort Grant in the summer of 1882. Several of his friends, Fred Dodge, Oregin Smith (Harelip Charley), Johnny Green, John Meagher, and one other, not identified (Lou Cooley) met him there.

Wyatt and Doc Holliday traveled to Arizona by stage, rail, and horseback to Hooker's ranch. When all of them had arrived, they moved out into the Chiricahuas and set up camp a little north of Galeyville. The reason for this was to protect their friend, Hooker.

Fred Dodge, the undercover king pin for Well's Fargo, had received the information that Ringo was riding to Galeyville from one of his informers. Dodge had strategically placed informers; i.e. Johnny O'Rourke, (Charleston gambler); Frank Leslie, (Oriental Saloon bartender); J. B. Ayers, (Charleston saloon owner); and Billy Breakenridge, (deputy sheriff). It was the latter who had passed the word on Ringo's whereabouts to Dodge and had received $100 in gold for the information.

Somehow the posse missed their quarry on the Galeyville trail, but back tracking, they found him as dusk quickly approached, camped a few miles from where his body was later found. Ringo had removed his gun and boots, and a small pot of coffee bubbled over a tiny fire. Apparently, he heard his enemies approaching; he grabbed his pistol and fled into the rocks up the canyon. Wyatt tracked him against the fading light; his rifle spoke once, effectively. As he was running higher up the canyon wall the trajectory of Wyatt's bullet passed thru the temple and out the top of the head.

Wild stories had been generated at the time of Curly Bill's demise and Wyatt did not intend that such would occur on Ringo's death. They hoisted him over his saddle and rode down the trail to a spot where black oak and white oak trees intertwined. There, near the trail, between the trunks of these trees, they placed Ringo's body, where it was sure to be found.

The posse then made a sweep through all the old outlaw haunts in the countryside down to Joe Hill's ranch in the hopes of flushing Ike Clanton, Pete Spencer, or even John Behan. Their primary mission accomplished and the others not to be found the posse returned to whence they came. Dodge, Smith, and Meagher to Tombstone; Lou Cooley to Hooker's ranch, and Wyatt and Doc to Colorado.

The Tombstone Weekly Epitaph, July 22,1882, carried the news of Ringo's death:

"DEATH OF JOHN RINGO

Sunday evening intelligence reached this city of the finding of the dead body of John Ringo near the mouth of Morse's Canyon in the Chiricahua Mountains on Friday afternoon. There were few men in Cochise County of Southeastern Arizona better known. He was recognized by friends and foes as a recklessly brave man who would go any distance or undergo any hardship to serve a friend or punish an enemy. While undoubtedly reckless, he was far from being a desperado, and we know of no murder being laid to his charge. Friends and foes are unanimous in the opinion that he was a strictly honorable man in all his dealings, and his word was as good as his bond

He was found by a man, named John Yoast, who was acquainted with him for years, both in this Territory and

Texas. Yoast is working for Sorghum Smith and was employed hauling wood. He was driving a team along the road and noticed a man in the midst of the clump of trees, apparently asleep. He passed on without further investigation, but on looking back, saw his dog smelling of the man's face and snorting. This excited curiosity and he stopped the team, and proceeded to investigate.

Mrs. Morse and Mrs. Young passed by where he was lying Thursday afternoon, but supposed it was some man asleep, and took no further notice of him. The inmates of Smith's house heard a shot about three o'clock Thursday evening, and it is more than likely that is the time the rash deed was done. He was on an extended jamboree the last time he was in this city, and only left here ten days ago. He had dinner at Diehl's in the South Pass of the Dragoons one week ago last Sunday, and went from there to Galeyville, where he kept on drinking heavily. We have not heard of his where - abouts after leaving Galeyvllle, but it is more than likely that he went to Morse's Canyon. He was subject to frequent fits of melancholy and had an abnormal fear of being killed.

Two weeks ago last Sunday in conversing with the writer, he said he was as certain of being killed as he was of being living then. He said he might run along for a couple of years more, and may not last two days. He was born in Texas and is very respectably connected. He removed to San Jose, California when about sixteen years old, and Colonel Coleman Younger, one of the leading citizens of that town, is his grandfather, Ringo was a second cousin to the famous Younger brothers now in the Minnesota Penitentiary for the partnership with the James boys. He has three sisters in San Jose, of which he was passionately fond. He was about thirty eight years old, though looking much younger, and was a fine specimen of physical manhood. Many friends will mourn him, and many others will take secret delight in learning of his death."

As usual, the information concerning Ringo was not valid. From this obituary, he appears to be the leading contender for the good citizen award. The difference in this Epitaph article and the ones in the past was that John Clum no longer controlled the paper. Sam Purdy was the new Epitaph editor and Sam was a Democrat and an ardent admirer of Ringo and the Cowboys.

To correct Purdy s blathering, Ringo was not an honorable man whose word was as good as his bond. Actually, he had skipped bond more than once. He was not born in Texas, but in Indiana. His sisters had rejected him completely.

He was not respectably connected. Colonel Younger was not his grandfather. There was no blood relation at all! Younger had married Ringo's aunt. He was related to the Younger's in no way other than his aunt's marriage.

Ringo should have looked younger than thirty eight years old as he was thirty two years old!

Those who do not believe that Wyatt and Doc came down from Colorado and killed Ringo point out that Doc was in court during that time period and Wyatt was in Gunnison.

True, Wyatt and Warren and some friends had been camping out on a creek not far out of Gunnison. One of them would come into town every few days to pick up supplies. During the time frame that it would have taken Wyatt to travel to Arizona, shoot Ringo and return to the Gunnison camp, there is no report, witness or newspaper item placing Wyatt in or near Gunnison or anywhere else for that matter.

Bat Masterson, a close friend of Wyatt's, was the marshal in Trinidad. A friend of his filed larceny charges against Doc Holliday. Every time this case came up, it was continued. It is obvious that this served as a means to prevent Holliday being extradited to Arizona. Later, it provided a proper alibi. The court cases referenced do not necessarily mean that Doc was present - only that he was represented. For that matter, any tall, skinny fellow could have appeared in court as Holliday as no one knew him during that time and place.

The newspapers of that time also reported very little about Holliday in Colorado. A Gunnison newspaper June 18,1882, placed Holliday there. Excerpts read:

"DOC HOLLADAY(sic) OF ARIZONA CAUGHT

ON THE WING BY A REPORTER AND PUMPED

> *There arrived in this city two days ago, a gentleman who has gained a great deal of notoriety within the past few weeks, through the columns of the press. The News Democrat's reporter's attention was first called to the gentleman by a businessman, who, pointing across the street said, "Do you see that man yonder? That's Doc Holiday (sic) of Arizona."*

When questioned, Holliday gave this answer:

> *"I shall probably be here until about the 30th when I have some business in Pueblo which will take me away for awhile, but I shall come back again and most likely remain in Gunnison City during the summer."*

It seems to be an unusual coincidence that Doc arrives in Gunnison about the time to start the trip to Arizona. He tells a newspaper reporter that he is going to Pueblo. But, does he? A Salida paper, dated July 8, 1882, carried a line concerning Holliday.

> *"Doc Holliday, late of Arizona, is in town in company with Osgood and Robinson. They will remain several days."*

It looks like Doc was late on his start to Arizona. But, then, this newspaper was discovered to have been a weekly paper and the item on Holliday was simply a reprint from the daily paper of July 3, 1882. This news item was included in the daily on July 1st or 2nd in order to be found and printed on the 3rd by the weekly edition. Nothing was said about Holliday in following issues.

Pueblo carried news on Doc on July 19, 1882:

> *"Doc Holliday, whose name was quite often before the public recently, is now in Leadville, and is being interviewed by the carbonate camp reporters.*

This did not pinpoint Doc as being anywhere in particular, just one town saying he was supposed to be in another town. The Leadville interview turned out to be a total of five words: "Doc Holladay (sic) is visiting Leadville." Some interview. Who saw him?

Even more interesting, the Leadville Daily Herald was owned by H. A. W. Tabor, a close, personal friend of Wyatt Earp, who would not have hesitated to help Earp and Holliday establish an alibi.

All newspaper and court records allow the necessary time for Wyatt and Doc to travel to Arizona and return to Colorado.

Fred Dodge always maintained that Johnny-Behind-the-Deuce killed Ringo - but he did that to protect his friend, Wyatt Earp and his company Wells Fargo. Some of Wells Fargo's actions could not become public knowledge and never will. Dodge was also a member of that final posse and could not implicate himself in the assassination of Ringo.

Many years later he changed his story and revealed the posse's chase, the shooting of Ringo, the placing of the body, and the posse disappearing as they had come. He no longer needed to protect his friend (Wyatt died in 1929) or Wells Fargo. And there was no one left who would prosecute him.

It appears that on several occasions Wyatt Earp received "blood money" for eliminating problems that irritated Wells Fargo. He was an employee of that company as well as served as a deputy U. S. Marshal at intervals almost all his life. It is a certainty that he had a hand in the destruction of all the people who killed Morgan and crippled Virgil. The only one to escape his wrath and vengeance was Pete Spencer. But that is the next book!

Ringo is believed by many to have been the deadliest, most feared gunman in all the west; though gunfighter he was not! And not much of any of the things that writers and tale-tellers have claimed him to be down through the years.

William "Bat" Masterson

Lifelong friend of Wyatt Earp. Served as lawman in several towns, buffalo hunter, gambler. Born in Fairfield, Illinois on November 24, 1853. Was working as a newspaperman on the Morning Telegraph when he died at his desk in New York City on October 25, 1921.

(Talei Publisher's photo)

Chapter XVI

NEW INFORMATION DISCOVERED

The following pages contain documents and photos that, in some circles, would be called the discoveries of the decade. However, the author is happy to just present them as items of history concerning Tombstone and some of its inhabitants during boomtown days.

This is the McLaury coat of arms as seen on the grave of William McClaughry in Ireland.

Arms: Per fesse, argent and azure in chief 3 hands, 2 and 1, gules, and in base, a fish swimming proper.

Crest: A swan with wings en-dorsed proper

Motto: Lamb Dearg Abuaidh (Red hand for Victory!)

The 3 red hands signify the 3 sons of Uh Nial, the first Viking leader to touch Ireland.

(courtesy Lee & Sherelyn McLaury)

This family coat of arms is found on the grave of William McClaughry in County Longford, Clonbroney, Parish St. Michael, Ireland. Records show that the name McLaughry was used in Iowa thru 1866, but by 1870 the spelling became McLaury.

(Courtesy Lee & Sherelyn McLaury)

Robert McLaury

Father of Tom, Frank, and Will, as he looked in later years.

(courtesy of Lee, Sherelyn, Doris & Shane McLaury)

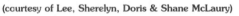

Robert Findley (Frank) McLaury

In Tombstone from a McLaury's photo album.

(courtesy of Lee, Sherelyn, Doris & Shane McLaury)

July 18, 1893, Bulletin-Journal, Thursday, Hazleton news:
(Independence, a bi-weekly newspaper)

"Robert McLaury died at his home in this place last Thursday night at 11:00 o'clock after a long illness. Will give further notice next week."

July 29, 1893, Bulletin-Journal, Thursday, obituary:

"Robert McLaury, who died here Thursday, July 6, was born in Kortright, Delaware County, New York, August 3, 1810, where he lived with his father until the 23rd year of his age when he came to Benton county, Iowa, where he lived ten years. He then moved to Belle Plaine where he studied law for 3 years. He was married to Margaret Rowland, Jan. 16, 1833. Eleven children were born of this union, five daughters and one son of whom are still living. His first wife died October 18, 1857, and October 11, 1875, he was married again to Mrs. Anna Leigh. Four children were the issue of this union –

Robert McLaury was the father of Frank and Tom McLaury.

three of whom together with the widow still survive him. He moved to this county in 1865 and bought 800 acres of land in Buffalo township. Eleven years ago he moved with his family to this town where he resided to the day of his death. He was an honest and respected citizen, a member of the Presbyterian church and died in the faith and full hope of salvation. He had been in poor health for some time although the end was not expected to soon, but during the last few days he failed very rapidly and soon breathed his last. None of the children by his first marriage were permitted to be present at the death of their father or at the funeral. The funeral services were held at the house on Saturday afternoon and were conducted by the pastor Rev. E. G. Beyer, after which the remains were laid to rest in the Hazleton Cemetery to await the glorious resurrection morning. The widow and children have the sympathy of their friends in their affliction."

Ebenezer McLaury

Frank and Tom's oldest brother

(courtesy Jim and Eileen Stevenson and Lee and Sherelyn McLaury)

Frank McLaury was wearing this buckle when he was killed in the gunfight at O.K. Corral. When Will McLaury returned home from Tombstone he brought Frank's gun and the belt and buckle that Frank was wearing. A grandson by Will's first marriage had the gun. Sometime in the 1930's it was lost or stolen. Shane's father, Stephen, had the belt and buckle, but a few years back the leather belt disintegrated. Shane owns this buckle.

(courtesy Lee, Sherelyn, Shane, & Doris McLaury)

(courtesy Lee, Sherelyn, Shane, & Doris McLaury)

Will McLaury built and owned this farm house and 800 acres of farmland in 1905. He moved from Ft. Worth to Lawton, Oklahoma in 1902. There he practiced law in a tent, working with settlers on filing claims and claim disputes when that part of Oklahoma was opened up for settlement.

Doris McLaury, wife of Stephen, grandson of Will McLaury.

Shane McLaury, son of Doris and great grandson of Will McLaury. Shane is 6'6", and owns Frank McLaury's belt buckle.

CLANTON-McLAURY GANG
or, THE COWBOYS
Tombstone, Ariz.

This photo comes from the album of Will McLaury's grandson. It is unfortunate that they are not clearly identified. The evidence with this photo and caption will be examined for identification by Earp historians (ones with credentials).

(courtesy Lee, Sherelyn, Doris, and Shane McLaury)

Holliday Water Right

Notice — Know all men by these here presents that we the undersigned, Citizens of the United States of America, do this day locate and claim all the waters in this Creek for Mining, Milling, Manufacturing Culinary and useful purposes, to be taken from its natural channel by ditch pipe or flumes and conveyed to any place we may think proper, to be used for the above purposes. Our notice of location is posted on a board seven inches by fifteen inches, nailed to a tree in the center of the Water Course and within ten feet of a dam and water ditch constructed by us on the left hand bank ascending, and all the waters of said creek turned in to said ditch, this dam and ditch is in Ramsey's Cannon about one and one half mile from mouth of said cannon in Cochise County, Arizona Territory and on the eastern slope of the Huachucha range. Said water right shall be known as the Holliday Water right — Located February the 3rd 1881

	Interest
Wyatt S Earp	" ¼ "
John H. Holliday	" ¼ "
Rich. B. Clark	" ¼ "
James Leavy	" ¼ "

Filed and recorded at request of R. B. Clark
Feby 5th A. D. 1881 at 8.30 A m
Geo R Drake
County Recorder.

Sister Mary Melanie Holliday

Many writers report a romance between this woman, who became a nun, and her famous cousin, John Henry "Doc" Holliday. This author has found no evidence of such a romance.

(courtesy of Bill Dunn)

John (Texas Jack) Wilson Vermillion

Born in 1842 in Kentucky, Jack was a Confederate cavalryman under Jeb Stuart from the beginning of the war. On his return from a visit home he ran into four Yankee cavalry men. He killed two of them and captured the other two. The sword in the photo is the one he carried in the war.

After the war he married a Horton girl, moved to Indiana then to Missouri. His wife and two children died in a diphtheria epidemic. Jack went out west.

Jack came to Virginia in 1883. He married Nannie Fleenor, had two more children and became a successful farmer with 2 farms. He died in his sleep in 1911.

(information and photo courtesy of Pete Hosey and John Vermillion, 88 year old grandson of Texas Jack)

Methodist church in Big Stone Gap, Virginia where Texas Jack was a Sunday school superintendent. He was also a member of the school board after he moved to Mendota.

He was called Texas Jack because he preferred a Texas breed of horses. He spent very little time in Texas.

It is said that he killed a man in a gunfight in 1890. Following that he moved to Mendota, 60 miles east. Reports say that he was barely five feet tall and a good friend of Doc Holliday's.

(photo and information courtesy Pete Hosey and John Vermillion)

Texas Jack's barn is still standing on the farm he owned.

(courtesy John Vermillion and Pete Hosey)

**Vermillion family reunion around the turn
of the century. Texas Jack is at extreme left.**

(courtesy John Vermillion and Pete Hosey)

**Texas Jack Vermillion and his second wife,
Nannie, about a year before his death.**

(courtesy Pete Hosey and John Vermillion, grandson of Texas Jack)

The Mendota Cemetery and
Texas Jack Vermillion's Tombstone.

(courtesy Pete Hosey and John Vermillion)

▲ Pete Hosey (left) and John Vermillion. Pete found the Vermillion family and John Vermillion who is the 88 year old grandson of Texas Jack.

▼ John Vermillion at his grandfather's grave.

Bibliography

I Married Wyatt Earp by Glen Boyer 1976

Wyatt Earp Tombstone Vendetta by Glen Boyer 1993

Wyatt Earp, His Autobiography by Glen Boyer 1981

The Street Fight by Michael Hickey 1992

Los Dos Pistoleros Earp by Michael Hickey 1993

The Cowboy Conspiracy to Convict The Earps by Michael Hickey 1994

The Private Journal of George W. Parsons Tombstone Epitaph 1972

The O.K. Corral Inquest by Alford Turner 1981

The Earps Talk by Alford Turner 1980

Tombstone's Epitaph by Douglas Martin 1963

Undercover For Wells Fargo by Carolyn Lake 1969

And Die in The West by Paula Marks 1989

The Truth About Wyatt Earp by Richard Erwin 1992

It All Happened in Tombstone by John Clum 1929

Wyatt Earp, Frontier Marshal by Stuart Lake 1931

Tombstone, a Iliad of the Southwest by Walter Burns 1927

Helldorado by William Breakenridge 1928

Newspapers

Arizona Weekly Star, Tucson

Sacramento Daily Record Union, Sacramento

Tombstone Daily Nugget, Tombstone

Tombstone Epitaph, Tombstone

Tombstone Weekly Nugget, Tombstone

Tucson Star, Tucson

Tucson Weekly Arizona Citizen, Tucson

Arizona Daily Star, Tucson

Tombstone Parables

- ❖ Trust everyone - but NEVER forget to cut the cards!
- ❖ May you be in heaven an hour before the devil knows you are dead.
- ❖ Tombstone is not the end of the world - but sometimes you can see if from here.
- ❖ Tombstone is a small town lying somewhere in that area between Peyton Place and the Twilight Zone.
- ❖ I'm too old to hope for new friends, but I would like a better class of enemies.
- ❖ A man should pay all his debts - be they debts of gratitude or revenge.
- ❖ All "wannabes" meet on the road to hell!
- ❖ For any strong and positive action a man is partly envied and partly hated - usually about evenly.

- ❖ May the Lord love us, but not call us soon.
- ❖ If you kill or maim an enemy, half the people will envy your courage - the other half will help hang you.
- ❖ To be popular in Tombstone - you must never be right or successful. That way the losers won't feel inferior.
- ❖ Mankind must surely be the Almighty's greatest mistake.
- ❖ I don't mind being judged on my knowledge of Tombstone by competent people - but I hate to be judged by people who can't find Schieffelin's monument.
- ❖ If you have no enemies you are a complete failure in life.
- ❖ A bad friend is worse than a good enemy.

- ❖ A "wannabe" author hanging out in and about Tombstone talks so much that he says things that he hasn't even thought of yet.

- ❖ Death cures bad habits.

- ❖ Death vastly improves the status of martyrs and outlaws.

- ❖ Keep your enemies close!

- ❖ Ladies, carefully close your window blinds - the Midnight Skulker is back in Tombstone.

- ❖ The friend of my enemy is also my enemy!

- ❖ Travel the road of life in such a manner that when you reach the end you won't wish that you had taken an alternate route.

- ❖ A man can best be judged by the enemies he makes.

- ❖ A friend is someone who knows you and still likes you.

- ❖ I take consolation from the fact that somewhere there is someone even worse than me.

- ❖ The older I get the harder it is for me to tell the good guys from the bad guys.

- ❖ Everyone was sent here for a purpose. What's yours?

ABOUT THE AUTHOR

The first Traywick to arrive in America was John, who land-ed in Charleston, South Carolina in 1662. He had two sons, John and James, the former eventually settling in Tennessee and the latter in Alabama.

Ben T. Traywick, a descendant of John Traywick, was born in Watertown, Tennessee on August 3,1927.

James Joseph Wiggins, Ben's maternal great-grandfather, was a private in the Confederate Army, Company B,16th Tennessee Infantry Regiment. Private Wiggins was killed in Perryville, Kentucky on October 8,1862.

Benjamin Abbot Traywick, Ben's paternal great-grandfa-ther, was a First Sergeant in the Confederate Army, Company G, 28th Infantry (2nd Mountain Regiment Tennessee Volunteers). Sergeant Traywick participated in all of the battles waged across Tennessee and Mississippi, from Chattanooga to Shiloh. At the end of the war, he resumed farming on acreage owned by the family.

Like his predecessors, Ben T. Traywick was military minded and enlisted in the U.S. Navy during World War II although he was only 15 years old, being tall for his age. Assigned to the U.S.S. Jenkins DD447 (Fletcher Class Torpedo Destroyer), attached to the amphibious forces in the Pacific, he had earned ten Battle Stars and a Presidential Citation by his eighteenth birthday. He served a second hitch in the Navy in the late 1940's, most of it in China. When the Communists overran

China, he was on the last ship to evacuate Tsingtao. The remainder of his enlistment was spent on the battleship Missouri.

Ben graduated from Tennessee Technological University with a B.S. Degree in Chemistry in 1953. After spending thirty years in exotic and high explosives in such places as Oak Ridge (Atomic); Sacramento (Missiles); and southeast Arizona (mining); he retired at the age of fifty-six.

Now he spends his time writing, researching Tombstone history, and visiting the far places in the American West and Mexico.

His first article was about a hillbilly sailor, called Saltwater McCoy. It was sold to "Our Navy" Magazine in 1957 and turned into a series. Ben has been frequently published in the Tombstone Epitaph since 1963. Since that beginning long ago, he has written more than six hundred newspaper and magazine articles. In addition, he has written forty four pamphlets and books. His collection of "Earpiana" and Tombstone material is one of the best in existence anywhere.

Having been duly appointed by the Mayor and City Council, Author Traywick is Tombstone's first and only City Historian to date. Ben and his wife, Red Marie, have lived in Tombstone since 1968. They have three children, Virginia Lynn, Mary Kate and William Maurice plus three grand children; Benton Ivan, Rachel Marie, and Joshua Cody. They are cofounders of the "Wild Bunch" and "Hell's Belles," now famous after twenty-seven years in the O.K. Corral and one hundred sixty-five films as of 1997.

Together, Ben and Marie have created the Tombstone Book Series, a number of volumes that depict the local history as it actually was. It is their wish that you will find these volumes interesting, entertaining and enlightening even as they have experienced them in writing them.

Red Marie & Ben Traywick